S. H. IRVINE

Applied Statistics (Continued)

GOULDEN · Methods of Statistical Analysis, *Second Edition*
HALD · Statistical Tables and Formulas
HALD · Statistical Theory with Engineering Applications
HANSEN, HURWITZ, and MADOW · Sample Survey Methods and Theory, Volume I
HOEL · Elementary Statistics
KEMPTHORNE · An Introduction to Genetic Statistics
MEYER · Symposium on Monte Carlo Methods
MUDGETT · Index Numbers
RICE · Control Charts
ROMIG · 50–100 Binomial Tables
SARHAN and GREENBERG · Contributions to Order Statistics
TIPPETT · Technological Applications of Statistics
WILLIAMS · Regression Analysis
WOLD and JURÉEN · Demand Analysis
YOUDEN · Statistical Methods for Chemists

Books of Related Interest

ALLEN and ELY · International Trade Statistics
ARLEY and BUCH · Introduction to the Theory of Probability and Statistics
CHERNOFF and MOSES · Elementary Decision Theory
HAUSER and LEONARD · Government Statistics for Business Use, *Second Edition*
STEPHAN and McCARTHY · Sampling Opinions—An Analysis of Survey Procedures

Regression
Analysis

A WILEY PUBLICATION IN APPLIED STATISTICS

Regression
Analysis

E. J. WILLIAMS, D.Sc.

New York · John Wiley & Sons, Inc.

London

Preface

THE CONSIDERABLE DEVELOPMENTS IN STATISTICAL METHODS and the increasing range of their application in recent years have led inevitably to a specialization of the subject matter. Thus the fields of experimental design and of sampling have already emerged as separate topics of study.

A treatise dealing specifically with the relations among two or more variables, and their applications in the interpretation of experimental results, seems to be long overdue. Many experiments either are designed to study the relations between variables, or depend on such relations for their interpretation. These and other applications are covered by the general methods of regression analysis.

Two sources of confusion have hindered the fruitful application of regression analysis to experimental data. One is the viewing of relations among variables in terms of correlations, which may be appropriate for the analysis of samples from homogeneous populations but not for experimental data, where interest lies in the estimation of one variable from another. The other is the confusion, more common among theorists than among practical experimenters, between regression relations, which have a wide range of validity and use, and functional relations, which are usually difficult to determine and are of limited usefulness.

The material presented in this book is based on the experience of analyzing experimental results, and has been included because the methods exemplified have been found useful in actual application. Since many of the interesting problems arise from the treatment of specific applications, I have attempted to relate the techniques to these applications and to indicate not only how the problem has arisen but also to what range of problems the given technique is applicable.

The book is addressed primarily to research workers in the experimental sciences. The problems with which it deals have arisen from consultation with such workers, and it is hoped that the material presented here will be not only intelligible to them but also useful in suggesting better ways in which their observations may be treated. Although most of the examples given are from the biological sciences, in which these statistical techniques have been most consistently developed, there is a growing need for, and awareness of, their value in the physical sciences and other fields; I therefore believe that workers in these fields will also find the material useful.

As there are now many excellent books on general statistical methods, it has been assumed that the reader is familiar with, or has ready access to, these methods. Accordingly, I have not presented the theory that is basic to the results given here. To have done so would have made the book unnecessarily long. For the same reason, I have not treated computational methods, although I am aware that computational methods in common use leave much to be desired. Since the book is addressed to experimenters rather than to mathematicians, the minimum of mathematics necessary to develop the methods is used, and the results are not always presented in their fullest generality or rigor. Nevertheless, the more mathematical equipment the experimenter has, the more effective use he will be able to make of the methods.

In the application of statistical methods to actual situations the logical problems must be kept in mind. It is not sufficient to be competent with techniques; we must know, too, the conditions in which a technique is both relevant and valid. I have attempted here to point out when a particular method is appropriate, how to make most effective use of the data, and the precautions to be taken in interpreting data. It is difficult to lay down general rules. Only a wide background of experience in dealing with experimental and observational data, and careful thought to drawing valid conclusions from them, can enable sure handling of these problems. Since practical situations will vary greatly, I have tried, while dealing with typical examples, to point to the principles underlying the approach, rather than to give general rules.

The plan of the book is somewhat novel. After the first four chapters, which deal with the determination of regression relationships, we turn in Chapters 5 and 6 to the important but seldom discussed questions of choice among regression formulas and the uses of the regression equation in estimation. Chapter 7, on the analysis of covariance, is the pivot of the book. The analysis of covariance, introduced as a variant of multiple regression, is further applied in Chapters 8, 10, and 11 in the development of significance tests for various multivariate problems. The approach used in these later chapters should prove helpful in bringing the treatment of important multivariate problems within the reach of experimenters and practical statisticians generally. These chapters deal with a wide range of topics—heterogeneous data, simultaneous equations, and discriminant functions. The final chapter, on linear functional relationships, is included to show the distinction between regression and functional relationships and to give some applications of the latter.

This book would not have been possible without the assistance of numerous friends who have posed problems, discussed methods of analysis, and read parts of the manuscript. To them I am indeed grateful. For many of the problems and practical examples I am indebted to research workers at the Division of Forest Products and other divisions of the Australian Commonwealth Scientific and Industrial Research Organization. For the assembling of suitable data, assistance with computing, and helpful comments I am especially indebted to Nell Ditchburne of the Division of Mathematical Statistics, C.S.I.R.O. The work presented in Chapter 9 was sponsored by the Office of Ordnance Research, United States Army.

E. J. WILLIAMS

Mackinac Island, Michigan
September 1959

Contents

CHAPTER   PAGE

1   INTRODUCTION 1
2   LINEAR REGRESSION 10
3   MULTIPLE AND POLYNOMIAL REGRESSION . . 23
4   REGRESSION EQUATIONS REQUIRING ITERATIVE
    CALCULATION 59
5   CHOICE AMONG REGRESSION FORMULAS . . 72
6   ESTIMATION FROM THE REGRESSION EQUATION   90
7   THE ANALYSIS OF COVARIANCE 117
8   THE TREATMENT OF HETEROGENEOUS DATA . 129
9   SIMULTANEOUS REGRESSION EQUATIONS . . 162
10 DISCRIMINANT FUNCTIONS 175
11 FUNCTIONAL RELATIONS 195
    REFERENCES 209
    INDEX 212

CHAPTER 1

Introduction

1.1 GENERAL

The subject of this book is one of the branches of statistics based on the method of least squares and the analysis of variance.   With the increase in the scope of statistical methods in recent years, certain fairly distinct branches have been developed to meet different needs.   Thus, on the one hand, the design of experiments is concerned with providing data from which the effects of various factors and the random errors affecting them can be most accurately and easily determined.   On the other hand, regression analysis enables the effects of various factors to be evaluated from the experimental data even when the experiment does not follow a simple pattern, or when the variables affecting the results cannot be controlled in such a manner as to make possible a designed experiment.

Thus, although the methods we shall consider can all be formally described in terms of the analysis of variance, it is more profitable to consider separately the problems in which the regression of one variable on others is of interest.   Clearly, such a method of analysis can be adopted, whether or not the data to be interpreted come from a designed experiment.   Where the experiment is designed to elucidate the effects of certain factors, the effects of other factors may be considered through a regression analysis, or by means of the technique of the analysis of co-variance, which enables the effects of uncontrolled variables to be allowed for and the accuracy of the experiment to be consequently improved.

In general, an experimenter who is to interpret rigorously the outcome of an experiment will need first to formulate the problem in mathematical terms (the mathematical model), then to test the concordance of the mathematical model in all relevant respects with the data, and finally, if the model proves to be acceptable, to estimate, or set limits on, any constants left unspecified in the model.   Regression analysis is a means of making such an interpretation when the expected value of one variable is defined as a function of the observed values of other variables.   Many physical laws, both theoretical and empirical, are of this nature when it

1

can be assumed that, for practical purposes, the variables are observed without error.   However, in the biological sciences, and indeed in all the sciences wherein the possibility of errors of observation is admitted, the idea of a relationship among errorless quantities turns out to be otiose, whereas the regression concept which bases relationships on the quantities actually observed proves to be exceedingly useful.

The testing of the concordance between theory and observation is based on probability considerations which give rise to significance tests; in general, if one of a set of unlikely outcomes, specified along with the mathematical model, is observed, the theory is rejected.   The role of tests of significance in the interpretation of data will be discussed later.

1.2   THE APPROACH TO THE INTERPRETATION OF EXPERIMENTAL DATA

Since statistical methods are effective only to the extent that they assist in the interpretation of observations, the choice of methods must always be based on a knowledge and appreciation of the conditions of the experiment.   Only thus can realistic theories be framed and an appropriate analysis made.   A mathematical formulation is often helpful in expressing the basic assumptions clearly and concisely, provided it also serves the end of a valid analysis of the data.

However, although it is helpful in any particular problem to formulate a mathematical model, the use of general models is to be discouraged; the student or experimenter, accustomed to thinking in terms of such general concepts, is liable to try to fit all experiments into one of the familiar models, rather than seeking out the unique characteristics of any particular problem.

In recent years there has been a tendency to treat statistical methods in greater and greater generality, as part of a more mathematical approach; often, however, this obscures the distinctive features of a problem.   We shall therefore often deal with particular cases that seem to be indicative of profitable lines of study, rather than presenting each problem in its fullest generality.

In particular, although many of the results of regression analysis and of multivariate analysis generally may be succinctly presented in matrix form, we have used matrix notation sparingly, in the belief that the interpretation is clearer when the results are set out in scalar notation.

1.3   SCOPE OF REGRESSION ANALYSIS

Regression analysis may be defined as the estimation or prediction of the value of one variable from the values of other given variables.   In the practical application of regression analysis, a number of interesting questions arise. First, there are the estimation of the constants of a regression when the form of the relationship is given and the testing of the concordance of some preassigned regression relation with the data. There is the related question of which variables should be included in the relationship. Once a regression relation has been established, we may use it to derive estimates, either of one of the variables, based on values of the others, or of the effects of the other variables on the one estimated. Again, the relationship may be used to improve the accuracy of estimates and of regressions by eliminating the effects of uncontrolled variables, as in covariance analysis.

A useful generalization of regression analysis is to the relations between two sets of variables. This includes on the one hand discriminant analysis, which turns out in its practical aspects to be the representation of variables of one set in terms of regressions on variables of the other set. On the other hand there is the determination of linear functional relations, important in certain practical problems such as calibration.

It may be noted here, and later chapters will confirm, that many of the practical problems arising in the interpretation of relations between two sets of variables are answered fairly directly by means of a regression analysis. Although much of the theory of multivariate analysis is somewhat sophisticated mathematically (see Anderson, 1958; Roy, 1957), it does not appear to be relevant to the general run of practical problems.

1.4 SIGNIFICANCE TESTS IN GENERAL

In the application of statistical methods to experimental data, we have to decide which observed effects are to be taken into consideration in the interpretation of the results. Since experiments, no matter how carefully controlled, are subject to error, we need to be able to distinguish effects that are due to the chance variation in the material from effects that arise from underlying differences. For instance, if a series of feeding experiments on sheep gives results showing that an increase of molybdenum intake is associated with a decrease in liver copper, at what stage is the experimenter justified in regarding the effect as real, rather than merely a manifestation of the random variation among his experimental animals? Clearly, in making judgments of this kind, some objective basis must be adopted. Such a basis is provided by tests of significance.

Because of their importance in inference, we devote the remainder of this chapter to considering some of the characteristics of significance tests. These points will be stressed because, in the practical applications of statistical methods, more trouble arises from ignoring basic points of principle than from neglect of the more elaborate techniques.

The role of significance tests in inference has been carefully set out by Fisher (1956), to which the reader is referred for a fuller discussion. Essentially, a significance test is a test, based on the observational data, of some hypothesis or theory.   Along with the hypothesis is specified a set of observational results which, according to the hypothesis, is of low probability.   If the observations give a result which belongs to this set, the test leads to the rejection of the hypothesis.   Naturally, such a test does not provide a full interpretation of the data.   It is simply a rule for deciding what evidence against the hypothesis is admissible.   When the evidence is already admitted on other grounds, or when the hypothesis is already untenable because of other considerations, the test of significance is irrelevant.

Significance tests have enabled experimenters to make inferences in an objective and orderly manner, unaffected by personal bias.   As a result, there has been a tendency to appeal to a significance test about almost every difference or relationship that is under examination.   One effect of this popularity of significance tests has been the proliferation of various tests for use in different situations.   Some of these tests are a welcome addition to the experimenter's armory of techniques; others, however, although valid as tests of some hypothesis, turn out not to be valid for supplying the answers to questions in which the experimenter is interested. In relation to any body of data we need to decide, therefore, first, whether a significance test is necessary to its interpretation, and, second, what the relevant test is.   In considering various tests during the course of this book we shall try to indicate the situations to which they are appropriate and the questions they can answer.

1.5   LIMITATIONS OF SIGNIFICANCE TESTS

The tendency to base the interpretation of data entirely on the results of significance tests has its dangers.   Many workers apply significance tests excessively, sometimes at the expense of sound judgment and a careful over-all assessment of the work.   A sound interpretation will take into account not only such individual tests as are made but also prior knowledge and experience and the general consistency of the effects that show up.

Thus, in analyzing the results of a study of the rate of fleece growth of four different breeds of sheep, some workers fitted polynomial trends to the relation of fleece length to time.   It was found that for some breeds a quadratic regression gave a satisfactory fit, the cubic term being non-significant, but that for other breeds a cubic regression was required However, with sets of similar data such as this, it is reasonable to assume that the regression relation is of the same form for each set.   It would therefore be reasonable to decide, on the basis of the data for all breeds together, whether the cubic term contributed to the fit of the curves and then to use either a quadratic or a cubic polynomial consistently for all the breeds.

Methods of making tests on combined sets of data will be discussed later, especially in Chapter 8. It is sufficient to say here, however, that numerous tests, of varying degrees of complexity, have been devised to test combined data or multiple comparisons from one set of data; yet it is seldom that their application results in much improvement over the exercise of good judgment and appeal to previous experience. Certainly their application without care and good judgment can give misleading answers.

A statement by Yates (1951) is worth quoting here:

The emphasis on tests of significance, and the consideration of the results of each experiment in isolation, have had the unfortunate consequence that scientific workers have often regarded the execution of a test of significance on an experiment as the ultimate objective. Results are significant or not and that is the end of it.

Research workers, therefore, have to accustom themselves to the fact that in many branches of research the really critical experiment is rare, and that it is frequently necessary to combine the results of numbers of experiments dealing with the same issue in order to form a satisfactory picture of the true situation.

1.6 PRIOR CONSIDERATIONS

Another point to note is that often prior considerations, or the conditions of the experiment, indicate that an effect or difference does exist. In that case not only is a significance test unnecessary but its use is unwise. An effect known to exist may yet be too small to be revealed by a significance test, so that the appeal to such a test leads to an apparent logical contradiction. It will mean the replacing of a decisive rejection of the hypothesis by a possibility of rejection, depending on the outcome of an experiment. Actually all that the test tells us is that the data provide no evidence for the existence of the effect; but such evidence, even if found, would be redundant.

The evidence which a significance test admits is, in general, of a less conclusive kind than that based on prior considerations. If we have no prior information about an effect, as in the comparing of a new treatment for the common cold with the standard treatment, we can draw conclusions only from a significance test. The hypothesis that there is no difference between the treatments is tenable and may even be supported by opinion; therefore any evidence against it must be derived from the observations alone, and the outcome will be uncertain, depending as it does on the size of the sample used, the inherent variability of the material, and the tests employed. On the other hand, if, for example, we are comparing different species of timber, we know that they differ in their mechanical and other properties; it may happen that, for two given species, some of these differences are rather small, but this does not justify our concluding, on the basis of some test of significance, that the species do not differ in these respects. In such cases what is of interest is some fiducial range within which the true difference may be expected to lie. Sometimes, with small observed differences, this range for the true difference will include zero, but this fact does not make such a range any less useful; the range still shows the extent to which the true difference is indeterminate.

1.7   STATISTICAL AND PRACTICAL SIGNIFICANCE

A distinction readily appreciated by the experimenter is that between the significance of an effect as determined by a statistical test and its practical importance when its existence is once established. For example, it may be that nutrition level affects the prevalence of twinning in sheep, the proportion of twin births being raised by improved nutrition from 10 to 12 per cent. The significance of such a difference could, of course, be established if a sufficiently large and well-controlled experiment were undertaken; however, in view of the wide range of conditions of nutrition and other environmental factors in animal husbandry, and the large effect of season, producing presumably even larger effects on the twinning rate, this difference would probably have no practical importance. The results of the significance test would then be ignored.

A careful experimenter who has some information about the inherent variability in his material will naturally aim to design his experiments so that the magnitude of differences or effects judged significant will be what is important in practice. This will mean that all the effects shown up by significance tests can be accepted, and that none of the information provided by the experiment is wasted.

1.8   INCORRECT APPLICATIONS OF SIGNIFICANCE TESTS

In order to throw further light on the uses of significance tests, we now discuss some examples to which the tests are incorrectly applied, owing to neglect of the principles just given. Often an experiment will be carried out using several levels of a quantitative factor, and the regression of response on level will be calculated. If the regression is linear, a particular relationship between response and treatment level may be taken to be established. Two inappropriate applications are sometimes made.

First, differences among individual response means may be tested. Now the significance of the regression has established the existence of a linear relation between response and level; hence, corresponding to any difference in level, however small, there will exist a difference in response. On the other hand, the difference between response means may well be non-significant for levels sufficiently closely spaced. A supplementary significance test on differences of means is therefore illogical and can be misleading. Second, calculations are sometimes made to determine what difference in treatment level is sufficient to produce a "significant" difference in response, or, rather, what difference in level can be tolerated without affecting the response significantly. As explained earlier, once a significant regression has been established, differences in response will exist between different levels, so that the "significance" of the difference is irrelevant. Probably what is required in such an analysis is the least difference in level that will produce a practically important difference in response. This is easily found as the ratio of the required difference in response to the regression coefficient on treatment level.

Another incorrect application is to adopt a hypothesis because a test of significance shows that there is no evidence against it. A typical example is in the fitting of a regression line when the constant term turns out to be small. If the constant term is found not to be significant, the test shows that a line through the origin is not discordant with the data, but it does not establish that this is the appropriate line. It is not correct to fit a line through the origin unless there is some prior reason for doing so. If, on the other hand, the null hypothesis specifies a line through the origin, it is appropriate to fit such a line unless a test shows that the hypothesis is discordant with the data. When the line is assumed to pass through the origin, the restriction on the variation of the line greatly increases the accuracy of determination of the regression coefficient; thus, to fit a line through the origin merely because the departure is nonsignificant gives a spurious appearance of accuracy to the regression.

Similar, although not so common, mistakes arise in fitting polynomial regressions, using either successive powers or orthogonal polynomials in the independent variable. It is not correct to omit terms merely because their contribution is nonsignificant, unless the null hypothesis specifies that the corresponding coefficients vanish.

These considerations show that significance tests have important but limited applications and are of most use in certain critical cases. Subsequent chapters will give numerous examples of their application, in which we shall endeavour to show their uses and limitations. These examples should make clearer the principles of inference outlined in the brief and rather abstract discussion just given.

1.9 FIDUCIAL LIMITS FOR PARAMETERS

The null hypothesis will often specify, among other things, the values of certain parameters; a significance test will indicate whether the specified values of the parameters are concordant with the data. In relation to any given parameter, it is convenient to consider a set of null hypotheses, differing from one another only in the value assigned to the parameter. The set of hypotheses that are not significant at the chosen level of probability P (say 0.01) will correspond in general to a range of values for the parameter, which will be called the $1 - P$ (i.e., 99 per cent) fiducial range; the limits of this range are called $1 - P$ (i.e., 99 per cent) fiducial limits.

This argument shows that, corresponding to any significance test of the value of a parameter, there will, in general, be a fiducial range of values; this provides a ready means of developing interval estimates for the parameter.

Simultaneous fiducial limits for two or more parameters may be defined in a similar way.   Some problems in the interpretation of such limits will be discussed in Chapter 6.

1.10 MULTIPLE COMPARISONS

One recent development has been the construction of simultaneous tests of several comparisons, in which the significance level is adjusted to make allowance for the fact that more than one test has been performed. The previous discussion shows that such tests, although they have achieved some prominence, will only rarely be needed.

Thus, in comparing the means for a number of different treatments, if an over-all F test is significant, this establishes the existence of treatment differences. If more detailed comparisons are required, individual treatments or combinations of treatments may be compared. However, the significance of the difference between two treatments is generally less important than a knowledge of a fiducial range for their difference—or, better still, a simultaneous fiducial range for all the treatment means, as described in the previous section.   This latter has been given by Fisher in his *The Design of Experiments* (Section 64).

However, it may occasionally be of interest to make multiple comparisons among several means.   The simplest test to use for this purpose is one proposed by Scheffé (1953).   This test has the advantage that it admits every possible comparison on an equal basis, and that its significance levels are readily derived from the significance points of the F distribution.

The test is based on the fact that, if there are m means to be compared, the maximum value of the sum of squares for any comparison is equal to the sum of squares between means, with $m - 1$ degrees of freedom. Accordingly, in applying Scheffé's test, we divide the sum of squares for the comparison of interest by $m - 1$ and compare it with the error mean square by means of the F test.

This test is clearly rather stringent and becomes more so as m is increased; the lack of sensitivity for any particular comparison is the price that has to be paid for the possibility of testing the significance of any comparison whatever, without regard for what comparisons are, a priori, likely to be of importance.

CHAPTER 2

Linear Regression

2.1 INTRODUCTORY

The linear regression relation, or straight-line relation between two variables, is probably familiar to all who have occasion to consider relations between variables. It requires only the most elementary techniques for its estimation. Nevertheless, it will be considered here in sufficient detail to bring out the basic principles of calculation and estimation, which can be applied to more complex forms of relationship.

For the purposes of this chapter we shall assume that n pairs of values of variables x and y have been observed, and that we are prepared to assume that there exists a linear regression of y on x; that is to say, the expected value of each value of y is a linear function of the corresponding value of x. The relationship may be written

$$E_x(y) = \beta_0 + \beta_1 x.$$

The two coefficients β_0 and β_1 are the regression coefficients, although β_0 is usually termed the intercept or constant term.

2.2 AN EXAMPLE

Example 2.1 Relation between Sodium Concentration and Flame Photometer Reading. For example, we may consider some data provided by the calibration of a flame photometer; these are given in Table 2.1. The photometer is designed to register the sodium concentration in a sample of material as a scale reading, the reading being roughly proportional to the sodium concentration. The samples were made up with preassigned sodium contents and the readings for each observed. In this instance, the scale reading is dependent on sodium concentration, so that the regression of scale reading on sodium concentration is appropriate. Inspection of the table shows that the constant of proportionality for the photometer is roughly 0.4. The calculations beneath the table (which will be discussed later) show that the regression coefficient b_1 estimated from these data is 0.416 and that the constant term is estimated as -0.89. Hence the regression equation is

$$Y = -0.89 + 0.416x.$$

10

This equation makes it possible to predict the scale reading corresponding to a given sodium concentration. If a scale reading is given and the sodium concentration is to be estimated, this equation may be transformed to give

$$X = (y + 0.89)/0.416$$
$$= 2.14 + 2.404y.$$

In this equation X has been employed to denote an estimated value. The equation is not the same as would have been obtained by calculating the regression of x on y; as x is a variable taking fixed values, however, it cannot have a regression on y, so that such a calculation would not be valid.

TABLE 2.1

SODIUM CONCENTRATIONS AND CORRESPONDING SCALE READINGS
OF A FLAME PHOTOMETER

Sodium Concentration, x, milliequivalents/liter	Scale Reading, y
25	10.0
50	20.0
75	29.5
100	39.5
125	52.0
150	62.0
175	72.0
200	83.5
225	91.5

Total	1,125	460.0
Mean	125	51.11
Sums of squares	37,500	6,495.889
Sum of products	15,600	
Regression coefficient		$= 15,600/37,500 = 0.416$
Constant term		$= 51.11 - 0.416 \times 125 = -0.89$
Sum of squares attributable to regression		$= 15,600^2/37,500 = 6,489.600$

2.3 DEPENDENT AND INDEPENDENT VARIABLES

In considering the relation between two physical quantities, it is usual to think of one variable as being the causal variable and to describe it as the independent variable, the other variable being dependent on it. In statistical analysis the same terms are used, but not in exactly the same sense. The dependent variable is the one whose values are distributed at random about the regression function, so that its *expected* value is some function of the *observed* value of the independent variable. The values of the independent variable need not be randomly distributed but may have been fixed or selected in any manner.

In the statistical sense, therefore, there is no implication that the independent variable is causal. Very often, however, values of the causal variable will be selected, so that the statistical and the physical definitions will agree. When sampling is random with respect to both variables, either variable may be regarded as independent as the one or the other is used to predict from.

2.4   ESTIMATION OF THE REGRESSION RELATIONSHIP

If the distribution of values of y about $E_x(y)$ is normal, it is known that the method of least squares is the efficient means of estimating the constants β_0 and β_1. The estimates, denoted b_0 and b_1, are then sufficient statistics for β_0 and β_1. Whether or not the distribution is normal, the method of least squares gives estimates whose distribution tends to normality the larger the size of the sample on which they are based. Consequently, the least-squares method of estimation will be used and it will be assumed that the estimates are distributed as though the underlying distribution of errors in the original data were normal.

The sum of squares to be minimized, with respect to the values β_0 and β_1, is

$$S(y - \beta_0 - \beta_1 x)^2,$$

where S denotes summation over the members of the sample. The minimization is usually carried out by means of the differential calculus, but it is worth notir g that it can be performed by elementary algebra, in a way which gives simultaneously the estimates of the two constants and the minimized sum of squares. This method of minimizing is, moreover, not confined to simple regression but may be extended to multiple regression equations. The sum of squares is

$$
\begin{aligned}
Sy^2 &- 2\beta_0 Sy - 2\beta_1 Sxy + n\beta_0{}^2 + 2\beta_0\beta_1 Sx + \beta_1{}^2 Sx^2 \\
&= Sy^2 - (Sy)^2/n - 2\beta_1(Sxy - SxSy/n) + \beta_1{}^2[Sx^2 - (Sx)^2/n] \\
&\quad + n(\beta_0 - \bar{y} + \beta_1 \bar{x})^2 \\
&= S(y - \bar{y})^2 - [Sy(x - \bar{x})]^2/S(x - \bar{x})^2 + n(\beta_0 - \bar{y} + \beta_1 \bar{x})^2 \\
&\quad + S(x - \bar{x})^2[\beta_1 - Sy(x - \bar{x})/S(x - \bar{x})^2]^2,
\end{aligned}
$$

where $\bar{x} = Sx/n$, $\bar{y} = Sy/n$.

From this partition of the sum of squares we see at once that: (i) Since the third and fourth terms, which alone depend on β_0 and β_1, are perfect squares whose minimum is consequently zero, the first two terms give the sum of squares of departures, minimized with respect to the values of the two parameters.

(ii) The third and fourth terms define the minimizing values of β_0 and β_1, which are found to be

$$b_1 = Sy(x - \bar{x})/S(x - \bar{x})^2$$

and
$$b_0 = \bar{y} - b_1\bar{x}.$$

(iii) The sum of squares accounted for by the regression on x, that is, the sum of squares indicating the departure of b_1 from zero, is obtained from the final term with β_1 put equal to zero; in general, the final term, with any assigned value of β_1, gives the sum of squares for the departure of b_1 from the hypothetical value β_1.

2.5 TESTING SIGNIFICANCE OF THE REGRESSION

This simple procedure thus gives the required estimates and opens the way for all the tests of significance based on the analysis of variance. If we write

$$(n - 2)s^2 = S(y - \bar{y})^2 - [Sy(x - \bar{x})]^2/S(x - \bar{x})^2,$$

then s^2 is an estimate of the residual variance of y, based on $n - 2$ degrees of freedom. The analysis of variance then takes the form shown in Table 2.2.

TABLE 2.2

	D.F.	Sum of Squares	Mean Square
Regression	1	$[Sy(x - \bar{x})]^2/S(x - \bar{x})^2$ $= b_1Sy(x - \bar{x})$ $= b_1^2 S(x - \bar{x})^2$	$b_1Sy(x - \bar{x})$
Residual	$n - 2$	$S(y - \bar{y})^2 - [Sy(x - \bar{x})]^2/S(x - \bar{x})^2$ $= (n - 2)s^2$	s^2
Total	$n - 1$	$S(y - \bar{y})^2$	

The analysis of variance for the example is given in Table 2.3. This analysis provides the test for the significance of b_1. Alternatively, the derivation shows that the standard error of b_1 is

$$\sqrt{\left[\frac{s^2}{S(x - \bar{x})^2}\right]}.$$

Fiducial limits for the value of β_1 may be derived using the value of b_1 and its standard error.

TABLE 2.3

ANALYSIS OF VARIANCE OF PHOTOMETER READINGS

	D.F.	Sum of Squares	Mean Square
Regression on sodium concentration	1	6489.600	6489.6
Residual	7	6.289	0.8984
Total	8	6495.889	

If t is the 1 per cent point of the t distribution with $n - 2$ degrees of freedom, the 99 per cent fiducial limits for β_1 are given as

$$b_1 \pm \frac{ts}{\sqrt{[S(x - \bar{x})^2]}}.$$

For the example, the standard error of $b_1 = 0.0049$ and $t = 3.499$ so that the fiducial limits are

$$0.416 \pm 3.499 \times 0.0049$$
$$= 0.399 \text{ and } 0.433.$$

2.6 TEST FOR THE INTERCEPT

One other aspect of the regression equation is often worth examining. In the example of calibration of a photometer it is reasonable to assume that the readings will be proportional to the actual sodium concentration. On this basis the regression equation would be

$$E_x(y) = \beta_1 x;$$

in other words, the constant β_0 giving the intercept on the Y-axis would be zero. For a test of the concordance of the data with this assumption, we need a different partition of the residual sum of squares from that given before. The sum of squares involving β_0 and β_1 is

$$n(\beta_0 - \bar{y} + \beta_1\bar{x})^2 + S(x - \bar{x})^2[\beta_1 - Sy(x - \bar{x})/S(x - \bar{x})^2]^2$$

which may be rewritten as

$$Sx^2\left[\beta_1 - \frac{Syx}{Sx^2} + \frac{\beta_0 Sx}{Sx^2}\right]^2 + \frac{nS(x - \bar{x})^2}{Sx^2}\left[\beta_0 - \frac{SySx^2}{nS(x - \bar{x})^2} + \frac{SxSyx}{nS(x - \bar{x})^2}\right]^2$$

$$= Sx^2\left[\beta_1 - b_1 + \frac{(\beta_0 - b_0)Sx}{Sx^2}\right]^2 + \frac{nS(x - \bar{x})^2}{Sx^2}(\beta_0 - b_0)^2.$$

The second term of this expression provides the criterion for testing the significance of any assigned value of β_0; in particular, if it is assumed that $\beta_0 = 0$, this term becomes

$$\frac{(SySx^2 - SxSyx)^2}{nSx^2S(x - \bar{x})^2} = \frac{nb_0^2S(x - \bar{x})^2}{Sx^2}.$$

This sum of squares may be tested against s^2 in the usual way; alternatively, the expression shows that the standard error of b_0 is estimated as

$$\sqrt{\left[\frac{s^2Sx^2}{nS(x - \bar{x})^2}\right]}.$$

Fiducial limits for β_0 may be determined using the value of b_0 and its standard error; a nonzero value would indicate that the instrument had a "zero error," for which an adjustment would have to be made.

For the photometer example, we have $b_0 = -0.89$. Such a negative value would not be a possible scale reading. We also have $Sx^2 = 178,125$, so that the standard error of b_0 is

$$\sqrt{\left(\frac{0.8984 \times 178,125}{9 \times 37,500}\right)} = \sqrt{0.4742}$$
$$= 0.69.$$

The ratio of b_0 to its standard error is $-0.89/0.69 = -1.29$, which is not significant. The assumption that the line passes through the origin is therefore acceptable.

To fit a line through the origin, the sum of squares to be minimized is simply

$$S(y - \beta_1 x)^2,$$

whence the estimate, denoted b_1' to distinguish it from the earlier estimate, is found to be

$$b_1' = Syx/Sx^2,$$

with variance

$$s^2/Sx^2.$$

In the present example,

$$b_1' = 0.4104$$

with variance

$$0.8984/178,125 = 0.000\ 005\ 044$$

so that the standard error of b_1' equals 0.00225.

It is noted that the standard error of the slope of the line through the origin is much less than that of b_1. This is generally true; the reason is that the assumption that the line passes through a given point contributes information which was not made use of in determining b_1; or, put in another way, the slope is restricted in its variation by the condition that the line passes through the origin.

On the assumption that the line passes through the origin, the 99 per cent fiducial limits for the regression coefficient are

$$0.4104 \pm 3.499 \times 0.00225$$
$$= 0.4025 \quad \text{and} \quad 0.4183.$$

2.7　LINEAR REGRESSION WITH GROUPED DATA

In many experiments a number of values of the dependent variable will be observed corresponding to each value of the independent variable. For example, an experiment may be repeated on a number of days, to improve the precision of the estimates for each value of the independent variable.　Again, it is sometimes convenient with large bodies of data to group the values of the independent variable into classes;　the values of

TABLE 2.4

	D.F.	Sum of Squares
Between groups, regression	1	$[S_r n_r \bar{y}_r(x_r - \bar{x})]^2 / S_r n_r(x_r - \bar{x})^2$
deviation from regression	$m - 2$	by subtraction
Total between groups	$m - 1$	$S_r n_r(\bar{y}_r - \bar{y})^2$
Within groups	$n - m$	by subtraction
Total	$n - 1$	$S(y - \bar{y})^2$

the independent variable will be replaced by the median values of the classes in which they fall, and to each class will correspond a varying number of values of the dependent variable.

When the values are repeated in this way, the sum of squares of the values of the dependent variable may be analyzed into parts corresponding to variation between groups and variation within groups, quite apart from any consideration of regression: if there are m groups, and n_r values in the rth group, whose mean is $\bar{y}_r$, the now-familiar analysis is

$$S(y - \bar{y})^2 = S_r n_r(\bar{y}_r - \bar{y})^2 + SS_r(y - \bar{y}_r)^2,$$

the corresponding partition of degrees of freedom being

$$\underset{\text{total}}{(n - 1)} \quad = \quad \underset{\text{between groups}}{(m - 1)} \quad + \quad \underset{\text{within groups}}{(n - m)}$$

The variation between groups can be further analyzed into that part attributable to regression on the independent variable and the residual not so attributable; we then have the analysis of variance shown in Table 2.4, in which x_r is the value of the independent variable for the rth group. The value of this form of analysis, rather than the simple analysis into regression and residual, is that it enables us to test the adequacy of the linear regression relation to represent the data. If the mean square for deviation from regression is significantly greater than that within groups, the hypothesis that the relation between the variables is linear must be rejected. It is then immaterial whether the regression is significant or not, since it does not satisfactorily represent the data. What alternative relationships may be fitted when a linear one is not satisfactory will be discussed in Chapters 3 and 4. The test for deviation from linearity will now be applied to a numerical example.

Example 2.2 Effect of Pressure in Sheetmaking on Tear Factor. In a laboratory experiment, which was repeated on four days, paper was made under five different pressures during sheet pressing. Various properties of the resulting sheets were recorded, including tear factor, whose values are given in Table 2.5. Since the variation between days was not significant, it has been ignored for this example.

TABLE 2.5

VALUES OF TEAR FACTOR AT DIFFERENT PRESSURES

Pressure	$2 \log_2 \left(\dfrac{\text{pressure}}{71} \right), x$	Tear Factor, y				Total	Mean
35	−2	112	119	117	113	461	115.25
50	−1	108	99	112	118	437	109.25
71	0	120	106	102	109	437	109.25
100	1	110	101	99	104	414	103.50
141	2	100	102	96	101	399	99.75

The pressures were chosen in geometric progression (with ratio $\sqrt{2}$) because it was expected that the properties would be approximately related to the logarithm of pressure; accordingly, in the second column of Table 2.5 are tabulated values of x, the logarithms of pressure to the base $\sqrt{2}$, reduced so as to have mean zero; the regression of tear factor on these logarithmic values was determined:

Sum of products $= -2 \times 461 - 1 \times 437 + 0 \times 437 + 1 \times 414 + 2 \times 399$

$$= -147$$

$$Sx^2 = 40$$

Regression sum of squares

$$= (-147)^2/40$$

$$= 540.22.$$

The analysis of variance given in Table 2.6 confirms the existence of the linear relationship and moreover shows that the pressure means do not depart from the regression relationship more than may be attributed to random error.

TABLE 2.6
Analysis of Variance of Tear Factor Values

	D.F.	Sum of Squares	Mean Square
Regression on log pressure	1	540.22	540.22**
Deviation from regression	3	28.58	$9.53^{(n)}$
Within pressures	15	492.00	32.80
Total	19	1060.80	

(n) Not significant
** Significant at 1 per cent level

2.8 TRANSFORMATION OF DATA BEFORE ANALYSIS

The regression analysis previously described may be validly performed provided (i) there is a linear relationship between the expected value of y and the value of x, and (ii) the variance of y about its expected value is the same for all x; in the two examples given these conditions were satisfied for all practical purposes. Fortunately, even when these conditions do not hold, it is very often possible to modify the original variables in some way so that the new variables satisfy the conditions. In Example 2.2, for instance, transforming the pressure to logarithms gave a satisfactory linear regression equation. (The fact that, in this particular case, the regression on untransformed pressure does not depart significantly from linearity, since the errors are high, does not affect the argument.) Very often, some transformation of one or the other variable will bring the relationship to linear form; the transformations most commonly employed are the logarithmic, the square root, and the reciprocal. Many examples may be found in the literature, so that it is not necessary to give examples here.

An example of a rather complicated relationship which may be reduced to linear form is Hankinson's formula for the failing stress in timber at various angles to the grain direction; this is

$$f_\theta = \frac{f_c f_c'}{f_c \sin^2 \theta + f_c' \cos^2 \theta}$$

where f_c is the stress parallel to the grain, f_c' is the stress perpendicular to the grain, and f_θ is the stress at an angle θ to the grain direction. This formula may be written

$$\frac{1}{f_\theta} = \frac{\cos^2 \theta}{f_c} + \frac{\sin^2 \theta}{f_c'}$$

$$= \frac{1}{f_c} + \sin^2 \theta \left(\frac{1}{f_c'} - \frac{1}{f_c} \right) ,$$

so that, if values of f_θ are observed for various values of θ, f_c and f_c' may be estimated from the constants of the linear regression of $1/f_\theta$ on $\sin^2 \theta$.

If we put $y = 1/f_\theta$ and $x = \sin^2 \theta$ and the regression equation is

$$Y = b_0 + b_1 x,$$

the estimates of f_c and f_c' are $1/b_0$ and $1/(b_0 + b_1)$ respectively.

The second condition, homogeneity of variance, is approximately satisfied for most sets of data in which the over-all variation of results is small compared with the error variance. If this condition does not hold, each value of the dependent variable must be weighted inversely as its variance for an efficient estimate of the regression coefficient to be obtained. The unweighted regression coefficient will still be unbiased, but it will be less accurately determined than the weighted coefficient. For this reason an efficient analysis is not possible unless the weights are known or can be estimated. If the weight of the values of y in the rth group is w_r, the weighted regression coefficient is

$$b_{1w} = \underset{r}{S} n_r w_r \bar{y}_r (x_r - \bar{x}) / \underset{r}{S} n_r w_r (x_r - \bar{x})^2,$$

and the sum of squares due to regression is

$$b_{1w} \underset{r}{S} n_r w_r \bar{y}_r (x_r - \bar{x}).$$

Sometimes the weights will be given independently of the values of x, but more often they are functions of x. For example, the variance of y is often proportional to the square of its expected value, that is, to $(\beta_0 + \beta_1 x)^2$, so that the appropriate weight is $(\beta_0 + \beta_1 x)^{-2}$.

When the variance of y is a function of its expected value, determination of the regression coefficient requires iterative methods, which will be discussed in Chapter 4. The method is to determine, by an unweighted analysis or some other approximate method, estimates of β_0 and β_1, and hence of the weights corresponding to each value of x. The analysis using these weights gives improved estimates, which by repeated application may be determined to any desired degree of accuracy. Usually two iterations are sufficient to reduce the error of calculation to a smaller order than the standard error of the estimates.

A simple case, which may be dealt with by the methods of this chapter, arises when the variance is known to be proportional to x^2. Then y/x has constant variance. Since the regression equation can be written

$$Y/x = b_1 + b_0/x,$$

the regression coefficient and constant term may be estimated from the regression of y/x on $1/x$. This case is illustrated in the following example.

Example 2.3 Fitting the Hankinson Formula to Experimental Data. As explained in Section 2.8, the Hankinson formula for the failing stress of timber at various angles to the direction of grain may be expressed as a linear relationship between the reciprocal of the failing stress and $\sin^2 \theta$. A set

TABLE 2.7

RELATIONSHIP BETWEEN MODULUS OF RUPTURE AND ANGLE OF GRAIN

Angle θ, °	Modulus of Rupture	10^6/M. of R., y	$\sin^2 \theta$	$1/(0.1 + \sin^2 \theta)$, x	$y/(0.1 + \sin^2 \theta)$, z
0	16,880	59.24	0.0000	10.00	592
2.5	14,720	67.93	0.0019	9.81	667
5	14,340	69.74	0.0076	9.29	648
7.5	12,740	78.49	0.0170	8.55	671
10	12,390	80.71	0.0302	7.68	620
15	7,140	140.1	0.0670	5.99	839
20	7,170	139.5	0.1170	4.61	643
30	4,710	212.3	0.2500	2.86	607
45	2,280	438.6	0.5000	1.67	731
60	1,720	581.4	0.7500	1.18	684
90	970	1,031	1.0000	0.91	937

Total				62.55	7,639
Sums of squares				129.2643	110,965
Sum of products				−1,849.87	

of experimental determinations of modulus of rupture at various angles to the grain direction is set out in Table 2.7. It was considered that the variance of the reciprocals would be approximately proportional to $(0.1 + \sin^2 \theta)^2$. Hence the weighted regression of 10^6 times the reciprocal of modulus of rupture y on $0.1 + \sin^2 \theta$ was determined. As explained earlier, this is equivalent to determining the regression of

$$z = y/(0.1 + \sin^2 \theta)$$

on

$$x = 1/(0.1 + \sin^2 \theta).$$

Accordingly, values of y, z, and x are also given in Table 2.7.

The regression coefficient of z on x, which is designated b_0, is

$$-1849.87/129.2643 = -14.31.$$

The constant term is

$$b_1 = \bar{z} - b_0\bar{x}$$
$$= 775.83.$$

Hence the weighted regression equation is

$$Z = -14.31x + 775.83.$$

Expressed in terms of y and $\sin^2 \theta$, the equation is

$$Y = -14.31 + 775.83(0.1 + \sin^2 \theta)$$

or

$$Y = 63.27 + 775.83 \sin^2 \theta.$$

As shown in Section 2.8, estimates of f_c and f_c' may be determined from this equation:

$$f_c = 10^6/63.27 \qquad = 15,800$$
$$f_c' = 10^6/(63.27 + 775.83) = 1190.$$

The analysis of variance, giving the residual mean square, is set out in Table 2.8. Note that, in this analysis, the significance of the regression on x is not

TABLE 2.8
ANALYSIS OF VARIANCE OF WEIGHTED VALUES, z

	D.F.	Sum of Squares	Mean Square
Regression on x	1	26,473	26,470
Residual	9	84,492	9,388
Total	10	110,965	

relevant, since the regression coefficient is related to the constant term in the regression of y on $\sin^2 \theta$.

The standard errors of the estimates are found as follows. Since

$$10^6/f_c = b_0 + 0.1b_1$$
$$= b_0(1 - 0.1\bar{x}) + 0.1\bar{z},$$

then

$$V(10^6/f_c) = 9388\left[\frac{(1 - 0.5686)^2}{129.2643} + \frac{0.01}{11}\right]$$
$$= 22.05,$$

and

$$\text{S.E. } (10^6/f_c) = 4.70.$$

Similarly,

$$10^6/f_c' = b_0 + 1.1b_1,$$

and

$$\text{S.E. } (10^6/f_c') = 55.1.$$

2.9   ALLOCATION OF VALUES OF THE
INDEPENDENT VARIABLE

The formula for the standard error of the regression coefficient b_1 shows that the precision of the estimate increases with $S(x - \bar{x})^2$; the greater the spread of values of the independent variable, and the greater their number, the more accurate the regression coefficient will be.   When it is possible to select values of the independent variable, it will be desirable to spread them as much as possible; theoretically the greatest spread will be obtained when the values are selected at the limits of the permissible range of the independent variable, half the values being at each limit. There are, however, practical objections to this procedure.   If only two values of the independent variable are sampled, it is not possible to tell whether the regression is in fact linear over the range.   For this reason it is preferable to allocate the values at several points throughout the range. For computational convenience it is often desirable to space the values equally.

These remarks may be summarized by saying that the optimum allocation depends on the use to which the data are to be put.   If the regression is known to be linear, allocation at the ends of the range is optimum; if information about the extent of departure from linearity is wanted, some method of spacing through the range will be optimum. However, it is seldom that the experimenter can specify in advance exactly what information he seeks from the data, so that it is not possible to define optimum allocation precisely.   Usually it is most convenient to take points equally spaced in the range considered and allocate an equal number of values to each.

CHAPTER 3

Multiple and Polynomial Regression

3.1 GENERAL

It is a natural extension of the idea of simple linear regression to consider the regression of one variable on several independent variables. The need for such a multiple regression relation may arise either from theoretical considerations, from the fact that the relation with any one independent variable does not give a high enough correlation to be of much value, or because the additional variables contribute substantially to an already high correlation. For example, it is known that the strength of timber depends on its density and its moisture content, so that in studying the mechanical properties of the material a regression relationship with these two variables would be sought. For most practical purposes a linear regression relation will be preferred.

In general, therefore, with a dependent variable y and p independent variables $x_1, x_2, \cdots, x_p$, we shall seek a relationship of the form

$$E_x(y) = \beta_0 + \beta_1 x_1 + \beta_2 x_2 + \cdots + \beta_p x_p.$$

Before setting out to determine a multiple regression equation, it is worthwhile to give some thought to the selection of independent variables. First of all, it is worthwhile to include only those variables that are thought likely to make an important contribution to the effectiveness of the relationship. Secondly, independent variables that are readily measurable or observable should be selected, both so that they can be used in deriving the estimated relationship and also, since the relationship may be required for later use in prediction, so that values can be determined for this purpose.

It is undesirable to include too many variables in the regression equation, first, because three or four variables if suitably chosen will generally provide a satisfactory relationship, second, because the work of calculation increases rapidly with the number of variables, and third, because an equation with many variables in it can seldom be easily applied in subsequent prediction.

23

3.2 ESTIMATION OF MULTIPLE REGRESSION

The same principles of estimation and testing of significance apply with multiple regression as apply with simple regression.   If we have a sample of n sets of values of the one dependent and the p independent variables, the sum of squares to be minimized is

$$S(y - \beta_0 - \beta_1 x_1 - \cdots - \beta_p x_p)^2.$$

We introduce at this stage the notation

$$u = S(y - \bar{y})^2$$
$$p_i = Sy(x_i - \bar{x}_i)$$
$$t_{ii} = S(x_i - \bar{x}_i)^2$$
$$t_{hi} = S(x_h - \bar{x}_h)(x_i - \bar{x}_i).$$

The sum of squares is then

$$u - \sum_i \beta_i p_i + \sum_i \beta_i(\beta_1 t_{i1} + \beta_2 t_{i2} + \cdots + \beta_p t_{ip} - p_i). \tag{3.1}$$

Then the normal equations found by differentiating (3.1) and replacing the β_i by their estimates b_i take the form

$$b_1 t_{i1} + b_2 t_{i2} + \cdots + b_p t_{ip} = p_i \qquad (i = 1, 2, \cdots, p),$$

or

$$\sum_h b_h t_{ih} = p_i. \tag{3.2}$$

The minimum value of the sum of squares of residuals, obtained when the constants β_i are given the values b_i, is

$$u - \sum_i b_i p_i.$$

This sum of squares, with $n - p - 1$ degrees of freedom, provides an estimate of the residual variance of departures from the regression equation and will accordingly be equated to $(n - p - 1)s^2$. The sum of squares attributable to regression is

$$\sum_i b_i p_i,$$

with p degrees of freedom.

The analysis of variance takes the form

	D.F.	Sum of Squares	Mean Square
Regression	p	$\sum_i b_i p_i$	$\sum_i b_i p_i/p$
Residual	$n - p - 1$	$u - \sum_i b_i p_i = (n - p - 1)s^2$	s^2
Total	$n - 1$	u	

which provides a test of the over-all significance of the regression. Usually the over-all significance will not be in doubt, but more detailed tests of the individual regression coefficients will be required, in order to assess the reality of the contribution of each variable. The ratio of the regression sum of squares to the total sum of squares (i.e., the fraction of the total sum of squares accounted for by the regression) is sometimes called the coefficient of determination and denoted by R^2. Its positive square root R is known as the coefficient of multiple correlation.

So far nothing has been said about the question of actually calculating the b_i. This question, and the determination of the standard errors, can be dealt with together. The equations (3.2) may be solved expeditiously by determining the reciprocal (inverse) of the matrix $T(= (t_{hi}))$. Various methods are advocated in the literature. In Example 3.1 we employ the method of Crout (1941), although other methods may be equally speedy. It is well, however, to standardize on one particular method unless the matrix to be inverted has special features that render it particularly amenable to some special method.

The inverse of the matrix T will be denoted by T^{-1} and its elements by t^{hi}. Then the b_i are given by the equation

$$b_i = \sum_h p_h t^{hi}.$$

It is readily shown that the variance of b_i is

$$s^2 t^{ii}$$

and that the covariance of any two coefficients, b_h and b_i, is

$$s^2 t^{hi}.$$

An immediate test may therefore be made of the significance of each regression coefficient, as soon as s^2 has been determined from the analysis of variance. Also, if the variables x_h and x_i are of the same kind, and it is considered likely that the regression coefficients b_h and b_i will not differ significantly, their difference may be tested against its standard error

$$s\sqrt{(t^{hh} - 2t^{hi} + t^{ii})}.$$

If it is valid to assume that the two regression coefficients are equal and if the significance test does not contradict this assumption, an average regression coefficient may be determined, as

$$\frac{b_h(t^{ii} - t^{hi}) + b_i(t^{hh} - t^{hi})}{t^{hh} - 2t^{hi} + t^{ii}}$$

with variance

$$\frac{s^2[t^{hh}t^{ii} - (t^{hi})^2]}{t^{hh} - 2t^{hi} + t^{ii}}.$$

If such an average regression coefficient were used, the sum of squares for regression would be reduced by the amount accounted for by the difference, namely

$$(b_h - b_i)^2/(t^{hh} - 2t^{hi} + t^{ii}).$$

TABLE 3.1

RECORDS OF BALLARAT DEW RETTING TRIALS 1942–1943, ON
VARIETY LIRAL CROWN

Mean Daily Rainfall during Retting Period, x_1, 0.01 in.	Retting Period, x_2, days	Mean Maximum Daily temperature during Retting Period, x_3, °F.	Ret Loss, y, per cent	
4.3	62	78	17.3	15.8
4.5	68	78	17.6	18.9
4.3	74	78	15.0	15.8
6.1	71	78	18.1	17.6
5.6	78	78	18.7	18.7
5.6	85	77	17.9	19.2
6.1	69	76	18.4	16.7
5.5	76	76	18.1	17.5
5.0	83	76	16.3	19.1
5.6	70	76	19.4	17.5
5.2	77	76	17.6	18.3
4.8	84	75	19.5	18.7
3.8	63	77	12.7	16.8
3.4	70	76	17.0	15.8
3.6	77	75	16.1	19.4
3.9	63	73	17.3	16.1
5.1	70	71	18.4	16.1
5.9	77	70	17.3	18.2
4.9	63	68	16.1	15.0
4.6	70	68	15.9	14.3
4.8	77	66	14.6	14.9
4.9	56	66	16.5	14.2
5.1	63	65	15.8	15.5
5.4	70	63	19.5	19.4
6.5	49	62	15.3	18.8
6.8	56	60	17.4	18.7
6.2	63	60	17.6	17.6

3.3 EXAMPLE SHOWING METHOD OF CALCULATION

Example 3.1 The Effects of Rainfall, Temperature, and Time of Exposure on Ret Loss of Flax. The data given in Table 3.1 are from a dew-retting experiment, in which flax was laid out under various climatic conditions and for various periods. Two samples were taken from each trial. The mean daily rainfall, mean maximum daily temperature, and retting period were taken as the independent variables. The sums of squares and products of deviations from the mean are calculated for each of the variables and are set out in Table 3.2. The method of Crout (1941), which is one of the methods

TABLE 3.2
SUMS OF SQUARES AND PRODUCTS OF VALUES IN TABLE 3.1

	x_1	x_2	x_3	y
x_1	40.2770	−65.489	−120.230	27.3193
x_2	−65.489	4097.33	1561.11	236.078
x_3	−120.230	1561.11	1943.70	66.193

also proposed by Banachiewicz, is used to invert the matrix and solve the equations. We first apply Crout's method to the determination of the regression coefficients and then show its more general application to the inversion of the matrix *T*.

3.4 EVALUATION OF REGRESSION COEFFICIENTS

The first steps in the solution consist of forming an auxiliary matrix (Table 3.3) from the original matrix, in the following way.

TABLE 3.3
THE AUXILIARY MATRIX

	x_1	x_2	x_3	y
x_1	40.2770	−1.625 97	−2.985 08	0.678 3
x_2	−65.489	3990.85	0.342 188	0.070 29
x_3	−120.230	1365.62	1117.51	0.046 32

1. The order of computations is to determine, first, the elements of the first column, then the remaining elements of the first row, the remaining

elements of the second column, the remaining elements of the second row, and so on until the auxiliary matrix is complete.

2. The first column of the auxiliary matrix is identical with the first column of the original matrix.

3. The first row of the auxiliary matrix, apart from the first term, is given by dividing the corresponding elements in the original matrix by the first element in the auxiliary matrix.

4. More generally, each element on or below the principal diagonal is equal to the corresponding element of the original matrix minus the sum of products of elements in its row and corresponding elements in its column in the auxiliary matrix that involve only previously computed elements.

5. Each element to the right of the principal diagonal is given by a calculation which differs from step 4 only in that there is a final division by the diagonal element in the auxiliary matrix.

For instance, the element in the third row and the second column

$$= 1561.11 - (-120.230)(-1.62597)$$
$$= 1365.62,$$

whereas the element in the second row and the third column

$$= [1561.11 - (-65.489)(-2.98508)]/3990.85$$
$$= 1365.62/3990.85$$
$$= 0.342\ 188.$$

Each element to the right of the principal diagonal is seen to be equal to the corresponding element below the principal diagonal, divided by a diagonal element; this fact reduces the computations considerably when the original matrix for the independent variables is symmetric. It is to be noted that the operations on the rows are carried right through to the final column, which is that of sums of products with the dependent variable.

The remaining step is to calculate the final matrix, which actually consists of the column of partial regression coefficients. The elements are determined in reverse order to the elements of the auxiliary matrix. We begin with the last element in the last column, in the auxiliary matrix, which becomes the last element in the final matrix. Each other element in the final matrix is equal to the corresponding element of the last column of the auxiliary matrix, minus the sum of products of elements in its row *in the auxiliary matrix* and corresponding elements in its column *in the final matrix* that have been previously computed.

As Crout points out, in forming products in the final matrix only those elements of the auxiliary matrix are used that lie to the right of the principal diagonal and to the left of the final column.

Thus, in the example, the final matrix is

$$0.9051$$
$$0.05444 \qquad (3.3)$$
$$0.04632,$$

the elements of which are the partial regression coefficients of ret loss on rainfall, time, and temperature respectively.

It is often desirable to carry a check column to ensure accuracy at each stage of the work. In the original matrix each element of the check column is the sum of the elements of the corresponding row. The check column is treated in the same way as the final column of the matrix. The check columns are:

Original Matrix	Auxiliary Matrix	Final Matrix
−118.123	−2.93276	1.90509
5829.037	1.41247	1.05444
3450.773	1.04632	1.04632

For the auxiliary matrix the check column checks the totals of elements to the right of the principal diagonal in each row.

3.5 INVERSION OF A SQUARE MATRIX

As Fisher (1954) points out, it is generally desirable to calculate, in addition to the actual regression coefficients, the solutions of three sets of simultaneous equations obtained by replacing the final column of Table 3.2 by, respectively,

$$\begin{bmatrix} 1 \\ 0 \\ 0 \end{bmatrix}, \begin{bmatrix} 0 \\ 1 \\ 0 \end{bmatrix}, \text{ and } \begin{bmatrix} 0 \\ 0 \\ 1 \end{bmatrix}.$$

The solutions of these three sets of equations actually make up the inverse of the matrix of sums of squares and products of the independent variables. In other words, if the solutions are

$$\begin{bmatrix} t^{11} & t^{12} & t^{13} \\ t^{12} & t^{22} & t^{23} \\ t^{13} & t^{23} & t^{33} \end{bmatrix},$$

then for Example 3.1

$$\begin{bmatrix} 40.2770 & -65.489 & -120.230 \\ -65.489 & 4097.33 & 1561.11 \\ -120.230 & 1561.11 & 1943.70 \end{bmatrix} \begin{bmatrix} t^{11} & t^{12} & t^{13} \\ t^{12} & t^{22} & t^{23} \\ t^{13} & t^{23} & t^{33} \end{bmatrix} = \begin{bmatrix} 1 & 0 & 0 \\ 0 & 1 & 0 \\ 0 & 0 & 1 \end{bmatrix}. \qquad (3.4)$$

These three sets of equations can be solved in the same way as the single set was solved, the three sets of solutions being arrived at simultaneously. The auxiliary matrix for this calculation is shown in Table 3.4.

Each column of this matrix is obtained from the corresponding column of the matrix on the right-hand side of (3.4) in the same way as the final column of Table 3.3 was obtained from the final column of Table 3.2. The final matrix, or inverse matrix, is given in Table 3.5.

TABLE 3.4
THE EXTENDED AUXILIARY MATRIX

$$
\begin{bmatrix}
40.2770 & -1.625\ 97 & -2.985\ 08 \\
-65.489 & 3990.85 & 0.342\ 188 \\
-120.230 & 1365.62 & 1117.51
\end{bmatrix}
\begin{bmatrix}
0.024\ 828\ 1 & 0 & 0 \\
0.000\ 407\ 42 & 0.000\ 250\ 573 & 0 \\
0.002\ 173\ 31 & -0.000\ 306\ 206 & 0.000\ 894\ 847
\end{bmatrix}
$$

The symmetry of the elements of the inverse matrix about the principal diagonal provides a check on the accuracy of the computations; if desired, a check column may be carried also, to ensure the accuracy of each step.

The use of the inverse matrix has several advantages. First, the regression coefficients are obtainable directly by multiplying the successive

TABLE 3.5
THE INVERSE MATRIX

$$
10^{-6} \times
\begin{bmatrix}
30{,}768.9 & -336.26 & 2{,}173.31 \\
-336.26 & 355.353 & -306.206 \\
2{,}173.31 & -306.206 & 894.847
\end{bmatrix}
$$

sums of products with the independent variable by the corresponding elements in a column of the inverse matrix.

Thus, the regression coefficient of ret loss on time is

$$10^{-6}(-336.26 \times 27.3193 + 355.353 \times 236.078 - 306.206 \times 66.193)$$

$$= 0.05444,$$

which agrees with the previous result.

If, as often happens, the regression of a number of dependent variables on the same set of values of the independent variables is required, the determination of the inverse matrix enables the calculation of the regression coefficients for each such variable to be performed without the solution of a set of equations in each case.

Second, as described earlier, the standard errors of the regression coefficients, and the correlations among them, are readily obtained from the inverse matrix.

3.6 STANDARD ERRORS OF THE REGRESSION COEFFICIENTS

To determine the standard errors of the regression coefficients, it is necessary to eliminate from the variation in the dependent variable the part that is attributable to the independent variables. The procedure for this analysis of variance is to calculate the sum of squares for regression, which is the sum of products of the regression coefficients and the corresponding sums of products of the dependent variable with each independent variable.

In the present example the regression sum of squares, with three degrees of freedom, is

$$27.3193 \times 0.9051 + 236.078 \times 0.05444 + 66.193 \times 0.04632 = 40.64 \quad (3.5)$$

The analysis of variance is set out in Table 3.6.

TABLE 3.6
ANALYSIS OF VARIANCE OF DATA IN TABLE 3.1

	D. F.	Sum of Squares	Mean Square
Regression	3	40.64	13.55
Residual	23	55.52	2.414
Duplicates	27	41.11	1.523
Total	53	137.27	

The effect of the three weather variates on ret loss is highly significant. The standard errors of the three regression coefficients are, in order,

$$\sqrt{(2.414 \times 30,768.9 \times 10^{-6})} = 0.273$$
$$\sqrt{(2.414 \times 355.353 \times 10^{-6})} = 0.0293 \qquad (3.6)$$
$$\sqrt{(2.414 \times 894.847 \times 10^{-6})} = 0.0465$$

Comparison of the regression coefficients (3.3) with their standard errors (3.6) reveals that the effect of rainfall is significant at the 1 per cent level and that of time is significant at the 5 per cent level, whereas that of temperature is not significant.

These standard errors and the significance tests based on them should, however, be interpreted with care. The significance tested is actually that of the additional amount of variation in ret loss accounted for by the variable considered, above that accounted for by the remaining variables.

Thus, for temperature, all that can be said is that the fit of the regression on rainfall and time, ignoring temperature, is not significantly worse than the fit of the regression on all three variables. In other words, the data supply no evidence that any effect that temperature may have is not adequately represented by the effect of rainfall and time.

The significance of the partial regression coefficients may also be tested by means of an analysis of variance. The sum of squares for the variation in ret loss accounted for by each individual variate, additional to that accounted for by the other two, is found by dividing the square of the partial regression coefficient by the corresponding diagonal term of the inverse matrix:

Sums of Squares for Partial Regression

Rainfall $\qquad \dfrac{10^6 \times 0.9051^2}{30{,}768.9} = 26.62$

Time $\qquad \dfrac{10^6 \times 0.05444^2}{355.353} = 8.34$

Temperature $\qquad \dfrac{10^6 \times 0.04632^2}{894.847} = 2.40$

The test of significance on these sums of squares is equivalent to that on the partial regression coefficients. It will be noted that these three sums of squares do not total to the sum of squares for regression given in Table 3.6. This is because the effects of the three factors are not independent. By subtracting the temperature sum of squares from the total regression sum of squares, we obtain the sum of squares for regression on rainfall and time, 38.24 with two degrees of freedom, which is clearly highly significant.

If we were to consider the simple regressions of ret loss on each factor, the other two factors being ignored, we should require a different set of sums of squares for testing significance:

Sums of Squares for Simple Regression

Rainfall $\qquad \dfrac{27.3193^2}{40.2770} = 18.53$

Time $\qquad \dfrac{236.078^2}{4097.33} = 13.60$

Temperature $\qquad \dfrac{66.193^2}{1943.70} = 2.25$

This shows that the temperature effect is not significant, even when other factors are ignored.

3.7 SHORT CUTS USING THE AUXILIARY MATRIX

For a rapid test of the over-all significance of the regression on the three variables, it will be found that the regression sum of squares can be obtained from the auxiliary matrix, as the sum of products of the diagonal elements with the squares of the corresponding elements of the final column; that is,

$$40.2770 \times 0.6783^2 + 3990.85 \times 0.7029^2 + 1117.51 \times 0.4632^2$$
$$= 18.53 + 19.71 + 2.40 \tag{3.7}$$
$$= 40.64.$$

Now in the expression (3.7) the first term is identified as the sum of squares for regression on rainfall, the other two factors being ignored. The last term is the sum of squares for regression on temperature, additional to that for regression on rainfall and time. It can be shown that the middle term is the sum of squares for regression on time, additional to that for regression on rainfall alone. In other words, the successive partial sums of (3.7) are the sums of squares for regression on one, two, and three factors, taken in the given order. This enables us to test the significance of adding new variables in the regression.

From similar considerations it can be shown that the successive elements of the last column of the auxiliary matrix are the regression coefficients in the regression involving only the variates corresponding to the previous elements of the column. Thus, the first element (0.6783) is the simple regression coefficient of ret loss on rainfall; 0.07029 is the partial regression coefficient on time, the effect of rainfall being eliminated; and 0.04632 is the partial regression coefficient on temperature, time and rainfall being eliminated.

These facts may be proved by considering the method of formation of the auxiliary matrix. Also it may be shown that the process of forming the final matrix from the auxiliary matrix is equivalent to eliminating from the regression coefficient on each variable the effect of the subsequent variables. The effect of the preceding variables having been eliminated in the auxiliary matrix, and that of the subsequent variables in the final matrix, it follows that the elements obtained are the required partial regression coefficients. A proof of the method of Crout along these lines, although less general in application, would be more closely linked with statistical concepts than the proof given by him, which is an inductive one.

3.8 ADDITION OR OMISSION OF INDEPENDENT VARIABLES BY CROUT'S METHOD

Methods of including or excluding an independent variable in multiple linear regression have been developed by Cochran (1938).   These methods obviate the need for resolving the normal equations each time a variable is added or omitted, simple adjustments to the existing inverse matrix and regression coefficients being all that are required.

The development of the auxiliary matrix in Crout's method makes the addition of new independent variables extremely simple.   To the original matrix are added rows and columns of sums of squares and products for the new variables.   The existing elements of the auxiliary matrix are unaffected; the new rows and columns, corresponding to the new rows and columns in the original matrix, are then calculated in exactly the same way as the existing elements of the auxiliary matrix were.   From this new auxiliary matrix the final matrix of regression coefficients may be calculated, but before this is done the significance of each additional variate in the regression can be tested by the method previously described, using the new elements of the auxiliary matrix.

Moreover, the final variable to be included is the one for which the auxiliary matrix gives the completely adjusted partial regression coefficient. This gives immediately the magnitude of the effect of the new variable, as well as its significance.

The omission of independent variables is even simpler, provided the variables to be omitted are the final ones considered.   From the auxiliary matrix are omitted those rows and columns corresponding to the omitted variates, and the final matrix is then determined as before.   Thus, if temperature were to be omitted from the regression, the auxiliary matrix of Table 3.4 would become

$$\begin{bmatrix} 40.2770 & -1.625\ 97 \\ -65.489 & 3990.85 \end{bmatrix} \begin{bmatrix} 0.024\ 828\ 1 & 0 \\ 0.000\ 407\ 42 & 0.000\ 250\ 573 \end{bmatrix}$$

and the final inverse matrix

$$10^{-6} \begin{bmatrix} 25,490.6 & 407.42 \\ 407.42 & 250.573 \end{bmatrix},$$

giving the regression coefficients

$$b_1' = 0.7926$$
$$b_2' = 0.07029.$$

Tests for the significance of each omitted variable would be made on sums of squares derived from the auxiliary matrix.

When the variable to be omitted is not the final one, the procedure is not quite so simple, for the regression coefficients on the subsequent variables, which are adjusted for that variable in the auxiliary matrix, have to be restored. Moreover, since the final and inverse matrices must be determined before the significance of the partial regression for the omitted variable can be tested, it is probably best to use the method to be described next in such cases. It is clearly desirable, if variables are to be omitted, to arrange them, as far as possible, in order of decreasing importance; this can sometimes, although not in general, be determined from the magnitude of the sums of squares for simple regressions.

Although the methods given here for addition or omission of variates are, in principle, the same as those given by Cochran, the procedure of working through the auxiliary matrix greatly simplifies the calculation of the inverse matrix. The method also lends itself more readily to generalization when a large number of variables is to be added or omitted.

3.9 THE OMISSION OR INCLUSION OF AN INDEPENDENT VARIABLE IN GENERAL

Besides the previously described method of eliminating an independent variable or including a new one, based on operations with the auxiliary matrix, there is a more general method which does not depend on the order in which the variables are excluded or included, and which was first described systematically by Cochran (1938). The general method is to make simple adjustments to the inverse matrix and the regression coefficients and is accordingly very easy to apply.

(i) Omission of a Variable

Suppose that there are p independent variables and that the one to be omitted is designated the pth. The elements of the inverse matrix of p variables will be denoted t^{hi} and the adjusted elements t'^{hi}; likewise the old and new regression coefficients will be denoted b_i and b_i' respectively. Then the adjustment formulas are

$$t'^{hi} = t^{hi} - t^{hp}t^{ip}/t^{pp}$$

and
$$b_i' = b_i - b_p t^{ip}/t^{pp}.$$

The second of these formulas is actually a simple consequence of the first. The reduction in the regression sum of squares due to the omission of the variable is clearly

$$b_p^2/t^{pp}.$$

(ii) Inclusion of a Variable

We denote the new variable by x_r $(r = p + 1)$ and, as before, the adjusted elements by a prime. In this case, besides adjusting the existing elements, we must also determine the new elements t'^{ir} and the new regression coefficient b_r'.   We therefore first determine the new elements:

$$t'^{rr}(t_{rr} - \sum_h \sum_i t^{hi}t_{hr}t_{ir}) = 1;$$

then

$$t'^{hr} = -t'^{rr} \sum_i t^{hi}t_{ir}$$

and

$$t'^{hi} = t^{hi} - t'^{hr} \sum_k t^{ik}t_{kr}$$

$$= t^{hi} + t'^{hr}t'^{ir}/t'^{rr}.$$

The b_i' may then be found, beginning with b_r', from the following formulas:

$$b_r' = \sum_i p_i t'^{ir}$$

$$b_i' = b_i + b_r't'^{ir}/t'^{rr},$$

which are clearly the converses of the formulas given in the previous subsection.

The increase in the regression sum of squares, due to fitting the additional independent variable, is

$$b_r'^2/t'^{rr}.$$

3.10 FIDUCIAL LIMITS FOR THE REGRESSION COEFFICIENTS

As in simple linear regression, fiducial limits may be determined for each of the coefficients in multiple regression. For each coefficient considered separately, the fiducial limits will be based on its standard error and the appropriate probability level of the t distribution; thus, for b_i the limits are

$$b_i \pm ts\sqrt{t^{ii}}.$$

Such limits for an individual coefficient are important when its departure from some hypothetical value is under test—in particular, for the test that the coefficient is zero. In multiple regression, however, it is often of interest to have simultaneous limits for all the coefficients, or at any rate for a set of them; for it is clear that the limits attained by each of the coefficients separately could not be attained by them simultaneously at the same significance level. These fiducial limits are readily determined in principle, although their detailed calculation may be difficult. Since the limits will consist of a curve or surface rather than a pair of points, they may be more clearly described as a fiducial boundary. The region enclosed will be called a fiducial region, as the generalization of a fiducial range in one dimension.

Consider the quadratic form

$$Q \equiv \sum_h \sum_i (b_h - \beta_h)(b_i - \beta_i)t_{hi};$$

this is a sum of squares with p degrees of freedom, so that the ratio Q/ps^2 is distributed as F with p and $n - p - 1$ degrees of freedom. Accordingly, to find the fiducial boundary for the β_i, at a given probability level, we take values of the β_i to satisfy the equation

$$Q = pFs^2.$$

The concordance of a given set of β_i with the data is similarly tested by whether the inequality

$$Q \leq pFs^2$$

is satisfied.

If the fiducial boundary for a set of the coefficients is required, the calculation is a little more complicated. Suppose that limits for the first r coefficients are required; let $(T^{-1})_r$ be the matrix consisting of the first r rows and columns of the inverse matrix T^{-1}, and let t_{hi}' be a typical element of the inverse of $(T^{-1})_r$. Then the quadratic form

$$Q' \equiv \sum_h \sum_i (b_h - \beta_h)(b_i - \beta_i)t_{hi}'$$

is a sum of squares with r degrees of freedom, so that the ratio Q'/rs^2 is distributed as F with r and $n - p - 1$ degrees of freedom. The fiducial region and its fiducial boundary may be determined using this distribution.

When $r = 2$, we have for the first two independent variables

$$t_{11}' = t^{22}/[t^{11}t^{22} - (t^{12})^2],$$
$$t_{12}' = -t^{12}/[t^{11}t^{22} - (t^{12})^2],$$
and
$$t_{22}' = t^{11}/[t^{11}t^{22} - (t^{12})^2];$$

hence to test the departures of β_1 and β_2 from zero

$$Q' = (t^{22}b_1^2 - 2t^{12}b_1b_2 + t^{11}b_2^2)/[t^{11}t^{22} - (t^{12})^2].$$

3.11 CORRECTIONS

A correction is any adjustment in the value of one variable to allow for the effect of the variation in a second variable. For example, the strength properties of most materials are affected by temperature. If a strength determination is made at some temperature other than the standard, it is customary to apply an empirical correction, given by the product of the departure of temperature from standard and a correction factor, to give the strength value that would be expected at the standard temperature. It will be clear that the correction factor in such an application is simply a regression coefficient; and from a suitably designed experiment in which strength values were determined at various temperatures, the correction factor could be determined. Here the assumption is made that the regression of strength on temperature is linear, an assumption which is near enough to base the correction on, especially if the correction is a small fraction of the measured value.

Sometimes, rather than determining the double regression of a variable y on two others (x_1 and x_2), it is found more convenient to correct one of the independent variables for variations in the other and to carry out a simple regression on the corrected variable. This procedure is satisfactory if the correction required is small, but otherwise it may give results that are somewhat artificial, since the corrected values of the independent variable may not correspond to observable quantities. It is actually appropriate when it is known or assumed that the second independent variable x_2 is uncorrelated with the dependent variable; the correction then plays the part of reducing errors in x_1 affecting the relationship of x_1 with y.

These two types of correction must be considered separately, since the calculations for the determination of each are different. However, for either type, the appropriate procedure, given a sample of values of each variable, is to determine the regression of y on x_1 and x_2, namely

$$Y = b_0 + b_1 x_1 + b_2 x_2.$$

(i) y to be Corrected for x_2

Here the appropriate correction factor is clearly the negative of the partial regression coefficient b_2. Indeed, for the sample values, the simple regression of $y - b_2 x_2$ on x_1 gives the regression coefficient

$$\frac{S(y - b_2 x_2)(x_1 - \bar{x}_1)}{S(x_1 - \bar{x}_1)^2} = \frac{p_1 - b_2 t_{12}}{t_{11}}$$

which, by (3.2),

$$= b_1,$$

the partial regression coefficient of y on x_1. Hence the adjustment using $-b_2$ gives here the same results as a double regression analysis.

Often, of course, values of y and x_2 are observed initially, and the y must be adjusted for the x_2, regardless of what later use will be made of the adjusted values. Then all that can be done is to take the simple regression of y on x_2. This will be satisfactory, provided any correlation between x_1 and x_2 is known to be fortuitous, and will on the average vanish. The correction factor will often be got in this way, or even be derived from one set of data and applied extensively to later work. These procedures are usually satisfactory as long as corrections are small.

(ii) x_1 to be Corrected for x_2

From the form of the regression equation, the appropriate correction factor is seen to be

$$c = b_2/b_1.$$

If the true correction factor is γ, then

$$b_2 - b_1\gamma$$

is distributed about zero with variance

$$s^2(t^{22} - 2t^{12}\gamma + t^{11}\gamma^2).$$

Hence fiducial limits for γ are given as the values for which F with 1 and $n - 3$ degrees of freedom is significant:

$$F = \frac{(b_2 - b_1\gamma)^2}{s^2(t^{22} - 2t^{12}\gamma + t^{11}\gamma^2)}.$$

Here, too, the correction factor will often be determined for one set of data and applied generally to subsequent sets. The fiducial limits for the true value therefore give some indication of the error likely to be introduced by general application of the correction.

In correcting x_1 for variation in x_2 we shall sometimes want to apply a correction regardless of what variable x_1 is to be correlated with. Here the negative of the regression coefficient of x_1 on x_2 would have to be used as the correction factor. It can be shown that this is exactly the same as the correction factor b_2/b_1, provided the simple correlation of x_2 with y is zero—in other words, provided x_2 is a variable introducing "errors" into x_1 but not affecting y. For then, since $p_2 = 0$,

$$b_2 = -p_1 t_{12}/(t_{11}t_{22} - t_{12}^2)$$

and

$$b_1 = p_1 t_{22}/(t_{11}t_{22} - t_{12}^2),$$

so that

$$b_2/b_1 = -t_{12}/t_{22},$$

the negative of the regression coefficient of x_1 on x_2. Thus the effect of the correction is to increase the regression of y on x_1 through its effect in reducing the errors in x_1 owing to the lack of control of x_2.

We now give an example of a correction applied to an independent regression variable.

Example 3.2 Determination of Total Solids in Skim Milk Concentrates by Means of a Refractometer; Adjustment of Results for Temperature Variation (Lawrence, 1955). In order to calibrate a refractometer for the determination of total solids in skim milk, a series of 55 samples was taken and refractometer reading and total solids were determined for each.

It was stated that refractometer readings should be adjusted for temperature, the correction factor being -0.08 per degree centigrade, so temperature was also recorded.

It is unnecessary to present the original data here. The regression equation for total solids y in terms of refractometer reading x_1 and temperature x_2 was found to be

$$Y = 1.33 + 0.9043x_1 - 0.057x_2,$$

and the covariance matrix for the regression coefficients (that is, s^2T^{-1}) was

$$10^{-6} \times \begin{bmatrix} 58.51 & -2.7 \\ -2.7 & 1048 \end{bmatrix}.$$

It is clear from these results that the coefficient b_2 is not significantly different from zero, its standard error being 0.032, and hence that the correction factor is not significant. However, it is of interest to determine the correction factor and its fiducial limits and to test its concordance with the given correction factor -0.08.

The 1 per cent point of F with 52 degrees of freedom is 7.15, so that the equation for the 99 per cent fiducial limits of γ is

$$7.15 = \frac{10^6(-0.057 - 0.9043\gamma)^2}{1048 + 5.4\gamma + 58.51\gamma^2},$$

which reduces to

$$817,400\gamma^2 + 103,050\gamma - 4243 = 0,$$

giving the limits as

$$-0.16 \quad \text{and} \quad +0.03.$$

Thus the given value -0.08 does not differ significantly from the value given by the data. In view of this, the given value of the correction should be used. The estimate of the correction factor from the data is

$$-0.057/0.9043 = -0.063.$$

In this example, since the standard error of b_1 is relatively small, it would be sufficiently accurate to derive fiducial limits for γ using the ratio b_2/b_1 and an approximate standard error. The approximate variance is given as

$$\frac{s^2}{b_1^4}(b_1^2t^{22} - 2b_1b_2t^{12} + b_2^2t^{11}) = \frac{10^{-6}}{0.6687} \times 857$$

$$= 0.00128,$$

whence the standard error is 0.0358, giving the same fiducial limits as were given before. The approximate method is very often sufficiently accurate, but the exact method just given is certain and is therefore more generally applicable.

3.12 CURVILINEAR (POLYNOMIAL) REGRESSION

The fitting of curvilinear regression equations defined by polynomials of the form

$$Y = b_0 + b_1x + b_2x^2 + \cdots + b_px^p$$

is in principle no different from the fitting of multiple regression equations as defined previously. The different powers of x simply play the role of the different independent variables in the earlier discussion. However, polynomial regression has some special features which merit separate consideration.

In the first place it should be pointed out that the fitting of polynomials of high degree to experimental or other data is seldom of much value. As Snedecor (1956, p. 470) says,

The student may well question the advisability of fitting curves. A stupendous amount of time has been wasted in ill-advised curve fitting. Only when the end in view is clear should the task be undertaken. Often a graph of the data points is sufficient. . . . Occasionally, fitted curves are required for interpolation. In many cases, graphical representation of the data is sufficient.

A polynomial is usually fitted in order to smooth out fluctuations in the data caused by random or uncontrolled errors, not because it is thought to represent the actual relationship. Unless the data show either a linear or a simple parabolic relationship, it may be equally satisfactory to smooth the data by plotting the points and drawing a freehand curve. The disadvantages of fitting freehand curves are, first, the possibility of systematic error caused by the unconscious bias of the experimenter and, second, the impossibility of making a valid estimate of the residual variation about the curve. The first objection can be overcome by experience and also by the freehand curves' being checked by another worker not likely to be similarly biased. The second objection is important only occasionally, and when it is some form of polynomial curve must be fitted by the method of least squares.

In the fitting of polynomial regressions, moreover, the significance of each of the regression coefficients cannot be tested in the same way as can the regression coefficients in multiple regression. The form the null hypothesis takes when a polynomial regression is being fitted is almost always that a polynomial of a certain degree represents the relationship, and the test of the hypothesis is whether terms of higher degree contribute significantly to the relationship. Hence, in fitting a relationship of this type, it is not open to us to omit any intermediate term, and indeed it is not valid to test such intermediate terms for significance. The first test to be made is an over-all test of whether the polynomial in fact gives a significant regression relation. What can then be done is to test the coefficient of the highest power, that of the next highest, and so on, successively; if there is no reason to the contrary, those that do not contribute significantly to the regression may be dropped from the equation. For example, if a cubic regression were being fitted, the first significance test would be of the over-all regression with three degrees of freedom; if this were not significant, there would be no need to make any further test. If the over-all regression is significant, the question arises whether the relationship may be adequately represented by a polynomial of lower degree; accordingly, the significance of the coefficient b_3 is next tested. If it is significant, the cubic regression relation will be accepted. If it is not significant, a quadratic regression may be fitted. It should be remarked that, when b_3 is dropped, all the other coefficients need to be recalculated. The quadratic coefficient will then be tested, to determine whether a linear or a quadratic relation is adequate. Tests can be made in this way for polynomial regressions of any degree.

There are, of course, exceptions to this procedure, for example, when the null hypothesis specifies a regression through the origin; then it would be correct to test the significance of b_0 before testing any of the other coefficients.

In practice, the mathematical form of a polynomial regression equation is seldom of importance except over long ranges of the independent variable; it is often impossible to distinguish fitted curves of different form, provided each has the same number of parameters, so that each can accommodate itself equally well to the trends in the data.

3.13   EXAMPLE ON THE FITTING OF A POLYNOMIAL REGRESSION

Example 3.3   Fitting a Quadratic Regression of Janka Hardness on Air-Dry Density of Timber Species.   The data shown in Table 3.7 are the mean values of Janka hardness for a number of species of timber, together with the corresponding values of mean density. It is known that the relationship between hardness and density is nonlinear, so a regression relationship of the form

$$Y = b_0 + b_1 x + b_2 x^2$$

has been fitted. The relevant sums of squares and products are shown in Table 3.8, from which the inverse matrix and the regression coefficients, shown in Table 3.9, are obtained. The analysis of variance is given in Table 3.10.

The regression equation is thus found to be

$$Y = -120 + 9.5x + 0.51x^2.$$

The standard errors of b_1 and b_2 are, respectively,

$$\sqrt{(26{,}170 \times 8519.198 \times 10^{-6})} = 14.9$$

and $\qquad\qquad \sqrt{(26{,}170 \times 0.937\,915 \times 10^{-6})} = 0.157.$

For the significance of b_2 we have $t = 0.509/0.157$

$$= 3.24 \text{ (significant at 1 per cent level)}.$$

Since the coefficient of x^2 is significant, the quadratic form of regression is retained. In this instance it is a reasonable assumption that the regression

TABLE 3.7

VALUES OF DENSITY, (DENSITY)^2, AND JANKA HARDNESS FOR
36 SPECIES OF TIMBER

Density, x, lb./cu. ft.	x^2	Janka Hardness, y	Density, x, lb./cu. ft.	x^2	Janka Hardness, y
67.4	4543	2700	40.7	1656	1100
68.8	4733	2890	66.0	4356	3260
69.1	4775	2740	59.8	3576	1940
57.3	3283	2020	39.4	1552	1210
24.8	615	427	59.2	3505	2310
32.7	1069	704	51.5	2652	2010
51.5	2652	1710	38.8	1505	1070
38.5	1482	914	53.4	2852	1880
46.9	2200	1400	35.6	1267	979
28.4	807	517	30.3	918	587
28.4	807	549	27.3	745	413
40.3	1624	1160	39.9	1592	989
29.0	841	648	56.0	3136	1980
56.5	3192	1820	40.6	1648	1010
42.9	1840	1270	69.1	4775	3140
40.7	1656	1130	57.6	3318	1980
24.7	610	484	45.8	2098	1180
48.2	2323	1760	39.3	1544	1020
			Total	1,646.4	81,747	52,901
			Mean	45.733	2,270.75	1,469.47

TABLE 3.8

SUMS OF SQUARES AND PRODUCTS OF VALUES IN TABLE 3.7

	x	x^2	y
x	6,454.66	609,545	371,186
x^2	609,545	58,628,500	35,595,200
			22,485,000

TABLE 3.9

INVERSE MATRIX AND REGRESSION COEFFICIENTS

$$10^{-6} \times \begin{bmatrix} 8519.198 & -88.571\,85 \\ -88.571\,85 & 0.937\,914\,7 \end{bmatrix}$$

b_i
9.474\,3
0.508\,631

line will pass through the origin. A direct test of the significance of b_0 can be made; or an equivalent test can be made by fitting a regression through the origin and testing the increase in the residual sum of squares for significance. Any significant departure of b_0 from zero will indicate either that the quadratic relation is not the true relation, that there is a "zero-error" in the hardness

TABLE 3.10

ANALYSIS OF VARIANCE OF JANKA HARDNESS

	D. F.	Sum of Squares	Mean Square
Regression	2	21,621,500	
Residual	33	863,500	26,170
Total	35	22,485,000	

TABLE 3.11

UNCORRECTED SUMS OF SQUARES AND PRODUCTS, FOR
DETERMINATION OF REGRESSION THROUGH ORIGIN

$$\begin{array}{ccc} x & x^2 & y \\ \begin{array}{c} x \\ x^2 \end{array} \left[\begin{array}{cc} 81{,}750.02 & 4{,}348{,}108 \\ 4{,}348{,}108 & 244{,}255{,}500 \end{array} \right] & \begin{array}{c} 2{,}790{,}525 \\ 155{,}720{,}100 \\ 100{,}221{,}600 \end{array} \end{array}$$

TABLE 3.12

INVERSE MATRIX FROM TABLE 3.11 AND REGRESSION COEFFICIENTS

$$10^{-6} \times \left[\begin{array}{cc} 230.028\ 51 & -4.094\ 846\ 5 \\ -4.094\ 846\ 5 & 0.076\ 988\ 379 \end{array} \right] \quad \begin{array}{c} b_i \\ 4.250\ 4 \\ 0.561\ 866 \end{array}$$

values, or that errors in the density measurement have reduced the regression coefficients from the values they would take if density were errorless. This last alternative is not likely, since density is accurately determined and is moreover determined on the hardness test specimens themselves.

The calculations for the regression through the origin are set out in Tables 3.11, 3.12, and 3.13. It is seen that the coefficient b_0 is not significant. Hence the regression through the origin is used:

$$Y = 4.3x + 0.562x^2.$$

It may be noted here that the test we have carried out is a test of the intercept of the regression line with the Y-axis; that is, a test of a possible zero error in hardness. In some applications it will appear that any departure from the origin will be due to a zero error in the independent variable. Then the same significance test for departure from the origin is

TABLE 3.13
ANALYSIS OF VARIANCE, FOR REGRESSION THROUGH ORIGIN

	D. F.	Sum of Squares	Mean Square
Regression	2	99,354,700	
Departure from origin	1	3,400	3,400[n]
Residual	33	863,500	26,170
Total	36	100,221,600	

[n] Not significant

appropriate, but different fiducial limits will be required. Suppose that the value of x for which Y is zero is denoted by ξ. Then the sample estimate of ξ is a root of the equation

$$b_2 \xi^2 + b_1 \xi + b_0 = 0$$

and fiducial limits for ξ will be given by the equation

$$(b_2 \xi^2 + b_1 \xi + b_0)^2 - t^2 s^2 [t^{22}(\xi^2 - \overline{x^2})^2 + 2t^{12}(\xi^2 - \overline{x^2})(\xi - \bar{x})$$
$$+ t^{11}(\xi - \bar{x})^2 + 1/n] = 0,$$

which is a biquadratic, giving four values of ξ.

These limits will have application in an experiment in which, for example, the regression of some quantity on time is being determined, but the exact starting time of the process cannot be recorded.

These methods may readily be extended to the fitting of polynomials of higher degree.

3.14 ORTHOGONAL POLYNOMIALS

When an equation of polynomial form is being fitted to data, it is usually convenient to include additional terms of successively higher degree in the equation until a satisfactory fit has been obtained; if a linear equation does not fit satisfactorily, a quadratic is tried, then if necessary a cubic, and so on. In this process the computations can be considerably simplified if the regression variables are chosen to be not the successive powers of the independent variable x but polynomials of increasing degree in x which are uncorrelated with one another in the sample. When the independent variables are defined in this way, the analysis is simplified because (i) each regression coefficient on each successive polynomial may be calculated independently of the others, as a simple regression coefficient would be calculated, and (ii) the sum of squares for regression attributable to each polynomial is likewise independently calculated and represents the amount by which the regression sum of squares is increased by the passage from an equation of lower degree to an equation of the degree of the polynomial. Thus, once the orthogonal polynomials are known, the contribution of any power of x to the fit of the regression can be readily determined.

For example, if the values of x were

$$1 \quad 2 \quad 5 \quad 8,$$

the successive orthogonal polynomials could be taken to be as follows:

				Sum of Squares
$\xi_1 = x - 4$				
-3	-2	1	4	30
$\xi_2 = (2\xi_1^2 - 2\xi_1 - 15)/3$				
3	-1	-5	3	44
$\xi_3 = (55\xi_1^3 - 95\xi_1^2 - 554\xi_1 + 300)/42$				
-9	14	-7	2	330

It is readily verified that these are uncorrelated in the sample; for instance,

$$S(\xi_2\xi_3) = 3 \times (-9) + (-1) \times 14 + (-5) \times (-7) + 3 \times 2 = 0.$$

Their sums of squares are shown in the right-hand column. Thus, if the corresponding values of y are

$$y_1 \quad y_2 \quad y_5 \quad y_8,$$

the sums of squares attributable to each increase of degree of the regression equation are as follows:

Linear $\qquad\qquad (-3y_1 - 2y_2 + y_5 + 4y_8)^2/30$

Quadratic $\qquad\quad (\ 3y_1 - y_2 - 5y_5 + 3y_8)^2/44$

Cubic $\qquad\qquad (-9y_1 + 14y_2 - 7y_5 + 2y_8)^2/330.$

Needless to say, the calculation of the set of orthogonal polynomials for every fitting of a curve is too laborious to be worthwhile. Although the numerical values of the polynomials just given are simple enough, the algebraic expressions for them are somewhat cumbersome and, of course, become more so as the degree of the polynomials increases. However, for many data the values of x are equally spaced and equally represented, and for these the values have been tabulated. Fisher and Yates (1953) give the polynomials of degree up to 5, for numbers of values of x up to 52. This range should be adequate for all practical requirements.

Example 3.4   Relationship between the Bursting Strength of Paper and Its Basis Weight. In Table 3.14 are given values of the mean bursting strength of paper made from standard Ljusnam kraft pulp beaten for 16,000 revolutions in the Lampen mill. The paper was made in nine different basis weights ranging from 10 to 90 grams per square meter, there being three replications of each. Although the bursting strength increases with basis weight, it obviously does not increase linearly, so a polynomial curve is sought to fit the data. The orthogonal polynomials for $n' = 9$, taken from Fisher and Yates's Table XXIII, are also set out in Table 3.14. The deviations from regression are tested against the estimated variance of means of three values, 3804 with 16 degrees of freedom, derived from the full analysis of the experiment. The calculations are given in the right-hand columns of the table. We see that deviations from a quadratic curve are highly significant, but that those from a cubic are not significant, so that a cubic curve provides a satisfactory fit to the data.

In order to use the regression function, it may be desirable to convert it into a polynomial in x explicitly. Fisher and Yates, in the Introduction to their tables, show how this may be done. However, for many purposes, it is equally convenient to work with the orthogonal polynomials ξ'. Thus, in the present example, the cubic regression equation is

$$Y = 4035.7 + 924.3\xi_1' - 1.5\xi_2' + 8.7\xi_3'.$$

Since the values of the ξ' are given, the estimated values corresponding to the experimental points are easily derived; thus, corresponding to $x = 40$, the estimated value is

$$4035.7 - 1 \times 924.3 - 17 \times (-1.5) - 9 \times 8.7 = 3059.$$

The estimates from the fitted cubic are given at the foot of Table 3.14.

The standard errors of estimates are also readily derived in terms of the orthogonal polynomials. In this example,

$$V(Y) = 3804\left(\frac{1}{9} + \frac{\xi_1'^2}{60} + \frac{\xi_2'^2}{2772} + \frac{\xi_3'^2}{990}\right).$$

At $x = 40$, $Y = 3059$, the variance is

$$3804\left(\frac{1}{9} + \frac{1}{60} + \frac{289}{2772} + \frac{81}{990}\right) = 1194;$$

$$\text{S.E. (3059)} = 34.6.$$

TABLE 3.14
MEAN BURSTING STRENGTH, y (GRAMS/SQ. CM.), AND BASIS WEIGHT, x, OF STANDARD LJUSNAM KRAFT PAPER, WITH ORTHOGONAL POLYNOMIALS

										$S(\xi'^2)$	$S(y\xi')$	b	Regression S.S.	Deviation from Regression		
														D.F.	S.S.	M.S.
y	360	1267	2146	3038	3962	5009	6114	6906	7519							
x	10	20	30	40	50	60	70	80	90					8	51,386,918	
ξ_1'	−4	−3	−2	−1	0	1	2	3	4	60	55,460	924.3	51,263,527	7	123,391	17,627**
ξ_2'	28	7	−8	−17	−20	−17	−8	7	28	2772	−4,296	−1.5	6,658	6	116,733	19,456**
ξ_3'	14	−7	−13	−9	0	9	13	7	−14	990	8,570	8.7	74,187	5	42,546	8,509[(n)]
ξ_4'	14	−21	−11	9	18	9	−11	−21	14	2002	−8,448	−4.2	35,649	4	6,897	1,724[(n)]
ξ_5'	4	−11	4	9	0	−9	−4	11	−4	468	−218	−0.5	102	3	6,795	2,265[(n)]

Fitted cubic

Y	418	1191	2086	3059	4066	5064	6009	6859	7569

[(n)] Not significant
** Significant at 1 per cent level

Two warnings should be given. The ease with which curves of high degree may be fitted by means of orthogonal polynomials may encourage indiscriminate curve fitting. It must always be remembered that, for many practical purposes, a hand-fitted curve is satisfactory.

The other point is that, because the regression coefficients and sums of squares may be determined separately for each orthogonal polynomial, it is easy to get the impression that a polynomial term of any degree may be fitted on its own. Thus, in Example 3.4, we might be tempted, since the regression on the quadratic polynomial was not significant, to fit only the linear and cubic terms. It must be clearly remembered that the polynomial of any given degree is constructed specifically to be orthogonal to all lower powers of x, in order that the sum of squares for regression on that polynomial may measure merely the contribution made by increasing the degree of the fitted curve to that of the polynomial. In fitting a curve, all orthogonal polynomials up to that of the highest degree fitted must be included, whether or not their contributions are significant.

3.15 EQUATIONS WITH COEFFICIENTS SUBJECT TO LINEAR RESTRICTIONS

Sometimes it is necessary to fit a regression relation in which the coefficients are restricted in order to satisfy some conditions. The simplest case, which has been dealt with already, is that in which one of the coefficients takes a fixed value; if the given value is zero, the variable corresponding to it is simply omitted from consideration; if the constant term is to be zero, so that the line (or, in general, the surface of higher dimension) passes through the origin, the correction for the mean is omitted. In testing hypothetical values of a set of the coefficients, we determine, in effect, the regression in which these coefficients are given their hypothetical values.

More complicated cases, although they do not occur frequently, are sufficiently important to be worth discussion. Several of the coefficients may have to satisfy a condition, which may be either linear or nonlinear. An example of coefficients required to satisfy a nonlinear condition arises in the fitting of concurrent regression lines, which is discussed in Chapter 8. More usually, the condition is linear, and only linear restrictions will be considered here.

As an example of a linear restriction, consider the estimation of the results of a destructive test from tests on neighboring specimens. In experiments in which it is required to estimate, say, the ultimate failing load of a specimen in order to test it under a reduced load, tests must perforce be made on adjacent specimens from the same material. Since the material is presumed to be homogeneous, it is natural to adopt an estimating equation, based on p neighboring specimens, of the form

$$Y' = b_1'x_1 + b_2'x_2 + \cdots + b_p'x_p,$$

where $b_1' + b_2' + \cdots + b_p' = 1$.

The x_i are the values of ultimate failing load in specimens located in the ith position in relation to the test specimen.

To determine the constants of this equation or to test the concordance of a given form of relationship with the data, tests must, in the first place, be made on the $p + 1$ specimens from a piece of material, including that at the location to be estimated. Subsequent tests to use the relationship would be made on only p specimens.

A further restriction would be made if the test specimen (giving the result y) were placed centrally with respect to the other specimens, in either one, two, or three dimensions. Then, by symmetry, the results for specimens in equivalent positions would be given equal coefficients. Such a case is illustrated in the accompanying diagram. These restrictions,

Two-Dimensional Symmetry

b_1	b_2	b_1
b_3	(y)	b_3
b_1	b_2	b_1

however, cause no difficulty, since their effect is to reduce the number of variables effectively to the number with different coefficients. Thus, in this diagram, one independent variable could be taken as the mean (or total) of results for the four corner elements, another as the mean for the top and bottom center elements, and so on.

In general, the linear restriction will not be so simple in form. We shall denote the unrestricted regression coefficients by b_i and the restricted coefficients by b_i'. We shall assume that a p-variable regression is to be determined, the coefficients being subject to the restriction

$$a_0b_0' + a_1b_1' + \cdots + a_pb_p' = k. \tag{3.8}$$

We may, in some cases, use the relation (3.8) to eliminate one of the unknown coefficients and then solve for the others. A more general method, which has the advantage of preserving the symmetry of the equations, is to introduce the Lagrangian multiplier λ and to proceed regardless of the restriction. The quantity to be minimized is then

$$S(y - b_0' - b_1'x_1 - \cdots - b_p'x_p)^2 + 2\lambda(a_0b_0' + a_1b_1' + \cdots + a_pb_p'),$$

leading to the normal equations

$$b_1't_{i1} + b_2't_{i2} + \cdots + b_p't_{ip} = p_i - \lambda(a_i - a_0\bar{x}_i). \tag{3.9}$$

In most practical examples a_0 equals zero, there being no restriction on the constant term in the equation. When a_0 is not zero, one possible procedure is to treat 1 as an independent variable and work with uncorrected sums of squares and products; alternatively, if corrected sums of squares and products are used, the a_i need to be corrected also, the corrected values being

$$a_i' = a_i - a_0 \bar{x}_i,$$

as shown in (3.9). Henceforth we shall assume, without any loss of generality, that $a_0 = 0$.

From the equations (3.9) the regression coefficients are found to be

$$b_h' = \sum p_i t^{hi} - \lambda \sum_i a_i t^{hi}$$

$$= b_h - \lambda q_h, \tag{3.10}$$

where $$q_h = \sum_i a_i t^{hi}.$$

Multiplying (3.10) by a_h and summing with respect to h, we find

$$k = \sum_i a_i b_i - \lambda \sum_i a_i q_i,$$

so that $$\lambda = (\sum_i a_i b_i - k)/\sum_i a_i q_i$$

and $$b_h' = b_h - q_h (\sum_i a_i b_i - k)/\sum_i a_i q_i.$$

It is readily confirmed that the restricted coefficients satisfy the condition (3.8).

The residual sum of squares is

$$u - \sum_i b_i' p_i - \lambda k$$

and the regression sum of squares is accordingly

$$\sum_i b_i' p_i + \lambda k.$$

Alternatively, the effect of the restriction must be to reduce the regression sum of squares by an amount representing the departure of the unrestricted coefficients from the condition required; this deduction from the sum of squares is

$$\frac{(\sum_i a_i b_i - k)^2}{\sum_i a_i q_i} = \lambda^2 \sum_i a_i q_i;$$

the residual sum of squares is increased by the same amount.

It is advantageous to express these results in terms of the unrestricted regression coefficients, because it will often be necessary to test the effect of the restriction in this way. The easiest way to determine the variances and covariances of the restricted regression coefficients is to recognize that they are linear combinations of the unrestricted coefficients. We have in particular

$$V(\lambda) = s^2 / \sum_i a_i q_i$$

and

$$\text{Cov}\,(b_i, \lambda) = s^2 q_i / \sum_i a_i q_i,$$

from which we find

$$V(b_i') = s^2 (t^{ii} - q_i^2 / \sum_i a_i q_i)$$

$$\text{Cov}\,(b_h', b_i') = s^2 (t^{hi} - q_h q_i / \sum_i a_i q_i).$$

These formulas are similar to those obtained when one independent variable is eliminated from a multiple regression. Indeed, the effect of the restriction is equivalent to that of eliminating from the regression the independent variable

$$X = \sum_i x_i q_i / \sum_i a_i q_i.$$

The sum of products of y with X is

$$\sum_i p_i q_i / \sum_i a_i q_i = \sum_i a_i b_i / \sum_i a_i q_i$$

and the sum of squares of X is $1 / \sum_i a_i q_i$, so that the simple regression coefficient of y on X is

$$\sum_i a_i b_i.$$

The sum of squares for the restriction is also the sum of squares for departure of this regression coefficient from its hypothetical value k.

Sometimes more than one restriction is imposed on the regression coefficients; the discussion just given may be generalized to such cases but need not be considered here, since no new principle is involved.

3.16 EXAMPLE OF A RESTRICTED REGRESSION RELATION

Example 3.5 Estimation of Test Values from Values for Neighboring Specimens. In an experiment planned to study the effect of duration of loading on small compression specimens of wood, it was decided to estimate their maximum short-time load and to apply a load which was a given fraction of the maximum. The estimates were derived from results for adjacent specimens used as controls, which were tested to failure in the usual way.

From each of a number of boards five end-matched specimens were taken, the specimens at the ends and middle being used as controls. In order to derive the regression equation, a series of determinations of maximum load on all five specimens from 114 boards was also made. The designation of the dependent variable (y) and the independent variables (x_1, x_2, and x_3) is shown in the following diagram:

$$x_1 \quad y \quad x_2 \quad - \quad x_3$$

and

$$x_3 \quad - \quad x_2 \quad y \quad x_1.$$

Each board provides two sets of values, as the diagram shows; the values of x_1 and x_3 have to be interchanged to correspond to the two values of y. In order to ensure that the estimator is homogeneous in the x_i, and that its mean equals the mean of y, we take

$$b_0' = 0$$

and

$$b_1' + b_2' + b_3' = 1,$$

so that

$$a_1 = a_2 = a_3 = k = 1.$$

Since the data are rather extensive, they are not given here, but the relevant sums of squares and products (uncorrected for the mean) are set out in Table 3.15.

TABLE 3.15
SUMS OF SQUARES AND PRODUCTS (UNCORRECTED) OF MAXIMUM COMPRESSIVE STRENGTH VALUES

	x_1	x_2	x_3	y
	12,061.5343	12,030.9275	12,032.6124	12,049.1993
$10^6 \times$	12,030.9275	12,047.2756	12,030.9275	12,041.8576
	12,032.6124	12,030.9275	12,061.5343	12,042.3124
				12,069.7072

In this example the corresponding values of all the variables are close together. The sums of squares and products uncorrected for the mean are therefore large and nearly equal, and their matrix is "almost singular," so that its inverse cannot readily be determined accurately. We can, however, reduce the size of the elements to give a matrix more amenable to calculation by means of a simple transformation of the variables. If we put

$$z_1 = y - x_1, \quad z_2 = y - x_2, \quad \text{and} \quad z_3 = y - x_3,$$

the equation

$$Y' = b_1'x_1 + b_2'x_2 + b_3'x_3$$

becomes

$$y - Y' = b_1'z_1 + b_2'z_2 + b_3'z_3.$$

The.equation in this form shows that b_1', b_2', and b_3' are to be chosen to minimize

$$S(y - Y')^2 = S(b_1'z_1 + b_2'z_2 + b_3'z_3)^2,$$

subject to the condition

$$b_1' + b_2' + b_3' = 1.$$

The uncorrected sums of squares and products of the z_i are set out in Table 3.16. If these are denoted by v_{hi}, the quantity to be minimized is

$$\sum_h \sum_i b_h'b_i'v_{hi} - 2\lambda \sum_i b_i'.$$

TABLE 3.16

SUMS OF SQUARES AND PRODUCTS OF NEW VARIABLES,
DERIVED FROM THOSE OF TABLE 3.15

	z_1	z_2	z_3
	32.8429	9.5778	10.8079
$10^6 \times$	9.5778	33.2676	16.4647
	10.8079	16.4647	46.6167

The normal equations are accordingly

$$\sum_i b_i'v_{hi} = \lambda,$$

giving for the regression coefficients

$$b_h' = \lambda \sum_i v^{hi}.$$

Hence

$$\lambda = 1/\sum_h \sum_i v^{hi}$$

and

$$b_h' = \sum_i v^{hi}/\sum_h \sum_i v^{hi}.$$

The inverse matrix and the regression coefficients are given in Table 3.17.

TABLE 3.17

INVERSE MATRIX, RESIDUAL SUM OF SQUARES, AND REGRESSION
COEFFICIENTS

				Sum	b_i'
	34,330.80	−7,203.87	−5,415.10	21,711.83	0.430 601
$10^{-12} \times$	−7,203.87	37,938.35	−11,729.38	19,005.10	0.376 919
	−5,415.10	−11,729.38	26,849.75	9,705.27	0.192 480
				50,422.20	

Residual sum of squares (226 D.F.) $= 10^{12}/50,422.20$
$= 19.8325 \times 10^6$

The residual sum of squares is

$$\sum_h \sum_i b_h' b_i' v_{hi} = \lambda \sum_i b_i'$$

$$= 1/\sum_h \sum_i v^{hi}.$$

This result is an example of a general theorem which we shall encounter again in Chapter 10. Let V be a $p \times p$ matrix of sums of squares and products with q degrees of freedom; then the reciprocal of the sum of the elements of its inverse is a sum of squares with $q - p + 1$ degrees of freedom.

In this example, $q = 228, p = 3$.

The residual sum of squares, as is shown in Table 3.17, is 19.8325×10^6 with 226 degrees of freedom, giving a residual mean square of $0.087\,754 \times 10^6$.

The estimated variances of the restricted regression coefficients are

$$V(b_i') = s^2(v^{ii} - b_i' \sum_h v^{hi})$$

$$= s^2 \left[v^{ii} - \frac{(\sum_h v^{hi})^2}{\sum_h \sum_i v^{hi}} \right].$$

Thus, $V(b_1') = 0.087\,754(34{,}330.80 - 21{,}711.83^2/50{,}422.20) \times 10^{-6}$
$$= 0.002\,192;$$

and similarly

$$V(b_2') = 0.002\,701,$$
$$V(b_3') = 0.002\,192.$$

Hence the standard errors of b_1', b_2', and b_3' are, 0.047, 0.052, and 0.047, respectively.

This method gives the restricted regression, which is what is required in practice. However, it may be considered necessary to test the significance of the effect of the restriction, in which case the unrestricted regression would also have to be fitted. In order to do this, an alternative transformation may be used.

The restricted regression of y on x_1, x_2, and x_3 is equivalent to the unrestricted regression of

$$y - x_3 \quad \text{on} \quad x_1 - x_3 \quad \text{and} \quad x_2 - x_3;$$

that is to say,

$$Y' - x_3 = b_1'(x_1 - x_3) + b_2'(x_2 - x_3)$$

is equivalent to

$$Y' = b_1' x_1 + b_2' x_2 + b_3' x_3.$$

Also the unrestricted regression of y on x_1, x_2, and x_3 is equivalent to the regression of

$$y - x_3 \quad \text{on} \quad x_1 - x_3, \quad x_2 - x_3, \quad \text{and} \quad x_3.$$

Hence, in this last regression, the partial regression of $y - x_3$ on x_3 provides a test of the effect of the restriction.

The transformation to the new variables has been made, reducing the sums of squares and products to more convenient quantities; these are given in Table 3.18. The inverse matrix for the three variables is given in Table 3.19.

TABLE 3.18
SUMS OF SQUARES AND PRODUCTS OF ALTERNATIVE VARIABLES
DERIVED FROM THOSE OF TABLE 3.15

	$x_1 - x_3$	$x_2 - x_3$	x_3	$y - x_3$
$10^6 \times$	57.8438	28.9219	-28.9219	35.8088
	28.9219	46.9549	-30.6068	30.1520
	-28.9219	-30.6068	12,061.5343	-19.2219
				46.6167

TABLE 3.19
INVERSE MATRIX AND REGRESSION COEFFICIENTS FOR
VARIABLES OF TABLE 3.18

				b_i
$10^{-12} \times$	24,986.93	$-15,377.10$	20.895	0.430 700
	$-15,377.10$	30,795.47	41.273	0.377 116
	20.895	41.273	83.0630	0.000 396

The regression coefficients (unrestricted) are those that would be given by these calculations, except that b_3 is now replaced by $b_3{}^* = b_1 + b_2 + b_3 - 1$. For the significance of the effect of the restriction, the sum of squares is

$$b_3{}^{*2}/t^{33} = 1900,$$

which is not significant. The significance is determined from the analysis of variance shown in Table 3.20.

Hence, to accord with logical requirements, the restriction that the sum of the coefficients equals unity is retained; the restricted coefficients may also be calculated by means of the formula for the omission of an independent variable:

$$b_1{}' = 0.430\ 700 - 20.985 \times 0.000\ 396/83.0360$$

$$= 0.430\ 600;$$

$$b_2{}' = 0.377\ 116 - 41.273 \times 0.000\ 396/83.0360$$

$$= 0.376\ 919;$$

by subtraction,

$$b_3{}' = 0.192\ 481.$$

Hence the estimation formula is

$$Y' = 0.431x_1 + 0.377x_2 + 0.192x_3,$$

agreeing with the result found earlier.

TABLE 3.20
ANALYSIS OF VARIANCE OF $y - x_3$

	D.F.	Sum of Squares	Mean Square
Regression on x_1, x_2, and x_3	3	26,786,000	
Residual	225	19,830,700	88,140
Total	228	46,616,700	
Due to b_3*	1	1,900	1,900[n]
Restricted regression	2	26,784,100	
Unrestricted regression	3	26,786,000	

[n] Not significant

As a simple example of a regression relationship with two restrictions we may consider the calculation of an equation of estimation independent of any linear trend in the values. It can be verified that this would require the restriction

$$-b_1'' + b_2'' + 3b_3'' = 0$$

on the coefficients, in addition to the original restriction. On account of the restrictions there is effectively now but one regression coefficient, and the analysis could be carried out as the simple regression (through the origin) of

$$y - \tfrac{1}{2}(x_1 + x_2) \quad \text{on} \quad x_1 - 2x_2 + x_3,$$

both new variates being adjusted for mean and trend; the regression coefficient is b_3''. The other two regression coefficients are then found as

$$b_1'' = \tfrac{1}{2} + b_3''$$
$$b_2'' = \tfrac{1}{2} - 2b_3''.$$

The sums of squares and products are then

$$S[y - \tfrac{1}{2}(x_1 + x_2)]^2 = 21.3165$$
$$S[y - \tfrac{1}{2}(x_1 + x_2)][x_1 - 2x_2 + x_3] = -0.2022$$
$$S[x_1 - 2x_2 + x_3]^2 = 129.9758$$
$$b_3'' = -0.001\ 556$$
$$b_1'' = 0.498\ 444$$
$$b_2'' = 0.503\ 112$$
$$Y'' = 0.498x_1 + 0.503x_2 - 0.002x_3.$$

The analysis of variance given in Table 3.21 shows that the effect of this second restriction is significant at the 1 per cent level; if it is necessary to make an allowance for trend, some worsening of the fit may be expected.

TABLE 3.21

ANALYSIS OF VARIANCE OF $y - \frac{1}{2}(x_1 + x_2)$

	D.F.	Sum of Squares	Mean Square
Regression on $x_1 - 2x_2 + x_3$	1	300	
Residual	227	21,316,200	
Total	228	21,316,500	
Effect of first restriction	1	1,900	
Second restriction	1	1,483,600	1,483,600**
Residual from Table 3.20	225	19,830,700	88,140
Residual from above	227	21,316,200	

** Significant at 1 per cent level

CHAPTER 4

Regression Equations
Requiring Iterative Calculation

4.1 GENERAL

The regression equations considered so far have been of a simple type: they have all been linear in the parameters to be estimated, or can be reduced to linear form. This has meant that the equations of estimation of the parameters have also been linear, and also that exact significance tests based on the assumption of normal variation have been applicable. However, it is often necessary to fit regression equations that are not linear in their parameters; for these, both the estimation of the parameters and the tests of significance are more difficult, and, in particular, exact significance tests are not possible. In this chapter, iterative methods of calculation suitable for such equations and approximate tests of significance for the values of the parameters will be presented.

As an example of a nonlinear equation which is reducible to linear form, consider the following:

$$Y = b_1(x - c) + b_2(x - c)^2,$$

which is nonlinear in c. The equation might be written in this form if the value of x for which Y is zero, here denoted by c, were of particular interest. This equation is, however, linear in

$$b_2 c^2 - b_1 c, \qquad 2b_2 c - b_1, \qquad \text{and } b_2;$$

for it may be written in the form

$$Y = b_2 c^2 - b_1 c - (2b_2 c - b_1)x + b_2 x^2.$$

Consequently, these three quantities may be estimated by the general methods for multiple linear regression, and joint fiducial limits for their true values determined. The question of determining fiducial limits for c will be discussed in Section 6.10.

On the other hand, the apparently simpler regression equation

$$Y = b_2(x - c)^2$$

cannot be reduced to a form linear in two parameters, and the methods of this chapter need to be applied in fitting it.

The simplicity of the estimation and testing of regressions linear in their parameters arises from the fact that (assuming, as usual, normal variation) there exists a set of jointly sufficient statistics for the parameters; this makes immediately applicable an analysis of variance, corresponding to the factorization of the probability into a part depending on the parameters and another part independent of them.

Only one general type of regression equation will be considered in this chapter, namely one that is nonlinear in one parameter, the most commonly occurring case.

The general form considered will be

$$Y = b_0 + b_1 f(x, c),$$

where f is some nonlinear function of c. Typical examples of frequent occurrence are

(i) $f(x, c) = e^{cx}$ (and variants r^x, x^c)

(ii) $f(x, c) = \log(x - c)$

(iii) $f(x, c) = (x - c)^t$, where t is known, and not unity; in particular $t = -1$.

The extensions to equations that are nonlinear in two or more parameters, for example,

$$Y = b_0 + b_1(x - c_1)^{c_2}$$

involve no new principle.

4.2 ESTIMATION OF THE PARAMETERS

In order to calculate the parameters by iterative methods, it is necessary first to choose some approximate value of c, so that the values of $f = f(x, c)$ can be calculated. An approximate value may be determined graphically or by other methods; no general method can be prescribed, but some methods will be demonstrated in working out the examples given in this chapter. Hartley (1948) has given some approximate methods that are suitable in certain cases.

If the adjustment to the preliminary estimate of c is δc, an improved value of f is given by

$$f + \delta c f',$$

where $f' = df/dc$. Then the regression equation becomes, to a first approximation,

$$Y = b_0 + b_1(f + \delta c f')$$
$$= b_0 + b_1 f + b_2 f',$$

where
$$b_2 = b_1 \delta c.$$

This is a linear regression on f and f', in which the ratio of the coefficients b_2 and b_1 gives the adjustment to c. Once the adjusted value of c has been determined, new values of f and f' need to be calculated, and the regression must be calculated again. Usually, if the initial estimate of c has been satisfactory, one or two cycles of iteration suffice to give all the accuracy required.

The standard errors of the coefficients may be determined in exactly the same way as for multiple linear regression, but it must be remembered that the standard errors are approximate only. They are probably satisfactory for rough significance tests; more exact tests have been proposed by Hotelling (1939) and developed for the particular case of exponential regression by Keeping (1951), but the increase in complexity of these tests is probably not warranted by the gain in accuracy.

A simple test of the concordance of a given value of c with the data is given by the significance of b_2, the partial regression coefficient of y on f'. This is an exact test since, as the null hypothesis defines the value of c, the regression is a linear regression on two *given* functions f and f'. There may be more powerful tests, however, since the linear regression makes no allowance for the nonlinearity of f as a function of c.

This test is to be distinguished from the test of significance of the regression of y on f. This is, of course, tested by the significance of b_1; as a total regression coefficient, if c is specified, or as a partial regression coefficient, if c is not specified but determined from the data. This latter test is, however, not exact.

Again, as for multiple linear regression, an analysis of variance may be set up, to give an approximate over-all test of the regression.

If s^2 is the residual mean square for y, and (t^{hi}) is the inverse matrix of sums of squares and products of f and f', then, approximately,

$$V(b_1) = s^2 t^{11},$$

and
$$V(b_2) = b_1^2 V(c)$$
$$= s^2 t^{22},$$

so that
$$V(c) = s^2 t^{22}/b_1^2.$$

4.3   FITTING AN EXPONENTIAL REGRESSION

In example (i) from Section 4.1, three different forms of exponential regression function, which can be reduced to the same form by various transformations of parameter or independent variable, were given. The first form is generally to be preferred, provided a table of e^x is available, as for this form

$$f' = xf,$$

so that once values of f have been tabulated, values of f' can be written down with a minimum of calculation. For this form of regression function, Stevens (1951) and Pimentel-Gomes (1953) have prepared tables which enable the calculations to be expeditiously carried out if based on equally spaced values of x. However, to illustrate the general principles, we give here an example in which the data are unequally spaced, so that Stevens' and Pimentel-Gomes' tables are not applicable. When data are equally spaced, it is advantageous to use Pimentel-Gomes' method, to which reference should be made.

Example 4.1   Relation between Daily Molybdenum Intake and Change in Total Liver Copper. Thirty sheep were selected from a homogeneous flock and divided at random into six groups of five animals each. The animals were all penned separately, and those of each group were fed the same amount of molybdenum in the diet, each group receiving a different level of molybdenum. The copper content of the liver of each sheep was determined by biopsy, both at the beginning of the experiment and after 27 weeks, and transformed to total liver copper by means of an empirical equation. The average daily molybdenum intake and average change in total liver copper for each group are presented in Table 4.1. The relation between molybdenum intake (x) and change in liver copper (y) was considered best represented by means of an equation that gave a diminishing effect as the intake increased, so the exponential relationship

$$Y = b_0 + b_1 e^{-cx}$$

was fitted.

Inspection of the first two columns of Table 4.1 showed that the constant b_0 was about -4.8; hence, corresponding to x values of 0.4 and 5.4, the values of $b_1 e^{-cx}$ are approximately 56.4 and 24.8. The ratio of these two values gives for a first approximation

$$e^{5c} = 56.4/24.8 = 2.274,$$

whence $c = 0.164.$

As a trial value, c was taken as 0.165. Values of f and f' for this value of c are tabulated in columns 3 and 4 of Table 4.1, from which the calculations follow. The calculations based on the preliminary estimate show that the standard error of c is 0.059, so that c need be determined to no more than three decimal places. In this example one cycle of iteration is sufficient, giving for c a final value of 0.166.

TABLE 4.1

CALCULATION OF EXPONENTIAL REGRESSION OF CHANGE IN TOTAL LIVER
COPPER, y (MG), ON DAILY MOLYBDENUM INTAKE, x (MG PER DAY)

$$f = e^{-cx} \qquad f' = -xe^{-cx}$$

x	y (mean of 5)	$c = 0.165$ f	f'	$c = 0.166$ f	f'
0.4	51.6	0.9361	−0.374	0.9358	−0.374
1.4	53.4	0.7937	−1.111	0.7926	−1.110
5.4	20.0	0.4102	−2.215	0.4080	−2.203
19.5	−4.2	0.0401	−0.781	0.0393	−0.766
48.2	−3.0	0.0004	−0.017	0.0003	−0.016
95.9	−4.8	0.0000	−0.000	0.0000	−0.000
Total	113.0	2.1805	−4.498	2.1760	−4.469
Sum of squares	3,835.63				

Calculation of first adjustment

$$\begin{array}{ccc} f & f' & y \\ \begin{bmatrix} 0.883\,685 & -0.537\,17 \\ -0.537\,17 & 3.518\,7 \end{bmatrix} & & \begin{matrix} 57.6546 \\ -34.882 \end{matrix} \end{array}$$

Inverse matrix

$$\begin{bmatrix} 1.247\,4 & 0.190\,43 \\ 0.190\,43 & 0.313\,267 \end{bmatrix} \qquad \begin{matrix} b_1 = 65.276 \\ b_2 = 0.0518 \quad \delta c = 0.0008 \end{matrix}$$

Calculation of second adjustment

$$\begin{array}{ccc} f & f' & y \\ \begin{bmatrix} 0.882\,782 & -0.537\,95 \\ -0.537\,95 & 3.483\,5 \end{bmatrix} & & \begin{matrix} 57.6248 \\ -35.201 \end{matrix} \end{array}$$

Inverse matrix

$$\begin{bmatrix} 1.250\,5 & 0.193\,11 \\ 0.193\,11 & 0.316\,889 \end{bmatrix} \qquad \begin{matrix} b_1 = 65.262 \\ b_2 = -0.0269 \quad \delta c = -0.0004 \end{matrix}$$

Regression sum of squares $= 57.6248b_1 - 35.201b_2$

$$= 3,761.66$$

The analysis of variance based on the fihal estimate of c is shown in Table 4.2. The sums of squares for groups and for regression are derivable from the data presented here; the sum of squares for error comes from the full analysis of the individual experimental results. The analysis shows that deviations from the fitted regression are not significant.

TABLE 4.2

ANALYSIS OF VARIANCE OF CHANGE IN TOTAL LIVER COPPER

	D.F.	Sum of Squares	Mean Square
Regression	2	3761.66	
Deviation from regression	3	73.97	24.66[n]
Total between groups	5	3835.63	
Error (within groups)	24	1108.80	46.20

[n] Not significant

The standard errors of b_1 and b_2 are determined in the usual way from the elements of the inverse matrix.   Thus

$$\text{S.E. of } b_1 = \sqrt{(46.20 \times 1.2505)} = 7.60,$$

and

$$\text{S.E. of } b_2 = \sqrt{(46.20 \times 0.3169)} = 3.83.$$

Hence

$$\text{S.E. of } c = 3.83/b_1 = 0.059.$$

The regression equation is then

$$Y = -4.85 + 65.3e^{-0.166x}.$$

4.4   FITTING A HYPERBOLIC REGRESSION

In Example (iii) listed in Section 4.1, the case when $t = -1$ gives a hyperbola.   The hyperbolic curve gives infinite values for Y when $x = c$; but usually, for observational data, all the values of x are on the one side of, and not close to, c.   If values of x close to c occur, so that very large values of Y (and hence of y) result, it may not be possible to maintain the assumption that the values of y are homogeneous in their error variation. For the present discussion we shall assume that all the values being considered are not too close to $x = c$, and that the errors are homogeneous.

The curve may be fitted by the general methods outlined, once a preliminary estimate of c has been chosen.   Had we considered the possibility of points in the neighborhood of $x = c$ being observed, a good preliminary estimate of c would be some value of x in the neighborhood of which large values of y were occurring.   As this possibility has been specifically ruled out from the present discussion on account of the other difficulties it raises, we need to find other ways of estimating c.

If, as sometimes happens, it is known that b_0 is zero, the regression equation can be written

$$Y^{-1} = (x - c)/b_1.$$

Consequently, if the reciprocal of y is plotted against x and a line drawn through the points by eye, the intercept of the line on the X-axis gives the first estimate of c. Alternatively, the regression equation of y^{-1} on x may be calculated, but this will usually be an unnecessarily elaborate means of obtaining c.

If b_0 is not zero, the equation may be rewritten

$$xY = b_0x + cY - b_0c + b_1;$$

hence, a first approximation to c may be found as the coefficient of y in the regression of xy on x and y. If this is considered too laborious a means of obtaining a preliminary estimate, a value must be in some way guessed from a plotted curve, or from previous knowledge of the particular problem.

Example 4.2 Calibration of a Stormer Viscometer. The Stormer rotational viscometer measures the viscosity of a liquid in terms of the time taken for a given number of revolutions of its inner cylinder. The actuating force is provided by a weight which may be varied. Theoretical considerations indicate a relationship between viscosity and time, of the form

$$\eta = (k_1w - k_2)t,$$

where η is the viscosity, w is the actuating weight, and t is the time. In calibrating the viscometer, liquids of known viscosity are used and the time for 100 revolutions recorded, so that viscosity here becomes the independent variable, and time the dependent. Also, different weights (20, 50, and 100 grams) are used, so that there are two independent variables, but there is still only one "nonlinear" parameter to be estimated. The regression equation may be written

$$Y = b_1x_1/(x_2 - c),$$

where now x_1 is viscosity, x_2 is weight, and y is time.

Putting

$$f = x_1/(x_2 - c),$$

we have

$$f' = x_1/(x_2 - c)^2;$$

we now have to determine a regression on f and f', but without any constant term, so uncorrected sums of squares and products are used.

The data of a calibration experiment are presented in Table 4.3; viscosities are in centipoises, weights in grams, and times in seconds. The necessary calculations are shown in and at the foot of the same table. Only one cycle of

TABLE 4.3
CALIBRATION OF A STORMER VISCOMETER

$$f = \frac{x_1}{x_2 - c} \qquad f' = \frac{x_1}{(x_2 - c)^2}$$

			$c = 2.6$		$c = 2.23$	
x_1	x_2	y	f	f'	f	f'
14.7	20	35.6	0.845	0.0486	0.827	0.0466
158.3	20	270.0	9.098	0.5229	8.908	0.5013
89.7	20	150.8	5.155	0.2963	5.048	0.2841
75.7	20	121.2	4.351	0.2500	4.260	0.2397
146.6	20	229.0	8.425	0.4842	8.250	0.4643
27.5	20	54.3	1.580	0.0908	1.548	0.0871
42.0	20	75.6	2.414	0.1387	2.364	0.1330
14.7	50	17.6	0.310	0.0065	0.308	0.0064
298.3	50	187.2	6.293	0.1328	6.245	0.1307
158.3	50	101.1	3.340	0.0705	3.314	0.0694
89.7	50	58.3	1.892	0.0399	1.878	0.0393
75.7	50	47.2	1.597	0.0337	1.585	0.0332
161.1	50	92.2	3.399	0.0717	3.372	0.0706
146.6	50	85.6	3.093	0.0652	3.069	0.0642
27.5	50	24.3	0.580	0.0122	0.576	0.0121
42.0	50	31.4	0.886	0.0187	0.879	0.0184
298.3	100	89.0	3.063	0.0314	3.051	0.0312
158.3	100	50.3	1.625	0.0167	1.619	0.0166
89.7	100	30.0	0.921	0.0095	0.917	0.0094
75.7	100	24.6	0.777	0.0080	0.774	0.0079
161.1	100	45.1	1.654	0.0170	1.648	0.0169
146.6	100	41.7	1.505	0.0155	1.499	0.0153
298.3	100	86.5	3.063	0.0314	3.051	0.0312
2796.4	1290	1948.6	65.866	2.4122	64.990	2.3289

Sum of squares 264,520

Calculation of adjustment

f	f'	y
315.379 4	13.928 68	9119.191
13.928 68	0.726 213	401.5331

Inverse matrix

0.020 734 4	−0.397 684
−0.397 684	9.004 54

$b_1 = 29.3977$**

$b_2 = -10.935^{(n)}$ $\delta c = -0.372$

(n) Not significant
** Significant at 1 per cent level

calculations is shown; examination of the standard errors shows that one cycle gives all the accuracy required. A further cycle of iteration does, in fact, alter the value of c to 2.22. The analysis of variance is given in Table 4.4, from which the standard errors are found to be

$$\text{S.E. of } b_1 = \sqrt{(39.4 \times 0.0207)} = 0.903$$
$$\text{S.E. of } b_2 = \sqrt{(39.4 \times 9.00)} \quad = 18.8$$
$$\text{S.E. of } c = 18.8/b_1 \qquad\qquad = 0.64.$$

TABLE 4.4

ANALYSIS OF VARIANCE OF RESULTS IN TABLE 4.3

	D.F.	Sum of Squares	Mean Square
Regression	2	263,692	
Residual	21	828	39.4
Total (uncorrected for mean)	23	264,520	

The regression equation is

$$Y = 29.40x_1/(x_2 - 2.22).$$

The value 2.22, whose departure from zero is highly significant, may be interpreted as the weight in grams required to overcome the internal friction of the viscometer.

4.5 LINEAR REGRESSION WITH ESTIMATED WEIGHTS

When the values of y corresponding to different values of x are subject to errors of differing variance, it is more efficient to use a weighted analysis than to analyze the data without weighting. The weight for any value of y will be inversely proportional to its variance. When the variances are unknown, they may be estimated from the data. This is practicable if, for example, there are corresponding to each value of x a sufficient number of values of y. Alternatively, and more commonly, it may be assumed that the variance is some simple function of η, the expected value of y. Often it is found satisfactory to assume the variance proportional either to the expected value or to the square of the expected value, but other assumptions may be made in special cases.

As mentioned in Chapter 2, a weighted regression in which the weights are not given but are estimated from the data generally requires iterative calculations. Usually it is postulated that the variance of the observed values of y is some given function of the expected value. Sometimes the estimates of variance provide further information about the regression coefficients, which should be taken into account in any exact analysis. The method of maximum likelihood[1]—by which the values chosen as estimates of the parameters are those that maximize the probability density of the observed sample, regarded as a function of the parameters—has certain optimum properties and in particular enables this additional information to be taken into account. The method of least squares, which has hitherto been employed, is appropriate when the variance is independent of the expected value, so that its estimation does not provide additional information; it may also be used as an approximate method even when the variance is a function of the expected value.

We consider a simple linear regression

$$\eta = \beta_0 + \beta_1 x$$

in which the variance of y is a given function of η multiplied by a scale factor, say

$$V(y) = [\sigma\phi(\eta)]^2.$$

For the logarithm of the likelihood we have

$$L = \text{const} - n \log \sigma - S(\log \phi) - \tfrac{1}{2}S(y - \eta)^2/\sigma^2\phi^2.$$

Now we may write

$$\frac{\partial \log \phi}{\partial \eta} = \frac{1}{\phi}\frac{\partial \phi}{\partial \eta} = \frac{1}{\phi}\frac{\partial \phi}{\partial \beta_0} = \psi,$$

so that

$$\frac{1}{\phi}\frac{\partial \phi}{\partial \beta_1} = \psi x.$$

---

[1] The maximum-likelihood method (see, for example, Rao (1952)) is generally formulated as follows: If L is the logarithm of the probability density of the observed sample, depending on parameters θ_1, θ_2, $\cdots$, etc., equations equal in number to the unknown parameters are derived by equating to zero $\partial L/\partial\theta_1$, $\partial L/\partial\theta_2$, $\cdots$. The estimates of the parameters derived from these equations are consistent, that is, converging in probability to the parameter values, and also efficient, that is, asymptotically of minimum variance. The negative of the matrix of expected values of second derivatives,

$$-\left(E\frac{\partial^2 L}{\partial\theta_h\,\partial\theta_i} \right)$$

gives the inverse of the variance-covariance matrix of the estimates. The method reduces to the method of least squares when the variation is normal, and exact significance tests based on the normal distribution can be made when the estimating equations are linear.

Then

$$L_0 \equiv \frac{\partial L}{\partial \beta_0} = S\psi[(y - \eta)^2/\sigma^2\phi^2 - 1] + S(y - \eta)/\sigma^2\phi^2,$$

$$L_1 \equiv \frac{\partial L}{\partial \beta_1} = S\psi x[(y - \eta)^2/\sigma^2\phi^2 - 1] + Sx(y - \eta)/\sigma^2\phi^2,$$

$$L_\sigma \equiv \frac{\partial L}{\partial \sigma} = \frac{-n}{\sigma} + \frac{1}{\sigma} S(y - \eta)^2/\sigma^2\phi^2.$$

For the second derivatives, only the negatives of the expected values are required; these expected values are set out in the following matrix:

$$- \begin{bmatrix} S\left(\frac{1}{\sigma^2\phi^2} + 2\psi^2\right) & Sx\left(\frac{1}{\sigma^2\phi^2} + 2\psi^2\right) & \frac{2}{\sigma} S(\psi) \\ Sx\left(\frac{1}{\sigma^2\phi^2} + 2\psi^2\right) & Sx^2\left(\frac{1}{\sigma^2\phi^2} + 2\psi^2\right) & \frac{2}{\sigma} S(\psi x) \\ \frac{2}{\sigma} S(\psi) & \frac{2}{\sigma} S(\psi x) & \frac{2n}{\sigma^2} \end{bmatrix}. \qquad (4.1)$$

We write w for the estimated value of $1/\phi^2$; then the first two equations of estimation are

$$S\psi[w(y - Y)^2 - \sigma^2] + Sw(y - Y) = 0$$
$$S\psi x[w(y - Y)^2 - \sigma^2] + Swx(y - Y) = 0,$$

which may be written

$$b_0 Sw + b_1 Swx = Swy + S\psi[w(y - Y)^2 - \sigma^2]$$
$$b_0 Swx + b_1 Swx^2 = Swxy + S\psi x[w(y - Y)^2 - \sigma^2]. \qquad (4.2)$$

For comparison, the least-squares equations would be

$$b_0 Sw + b_1 Swx = Swy$$
$$b_0 Swx + b_1 Swx^2 = Swxy,$$

giving slightly different values, not only for b_0 and b_1 but also for the weights w. The second terms on the right-hand side of (4.2) are adjustments to enable the information provided by the variance estimates $(y - b_0 - b_1 x)^2$ to be included.

In the information matrix (4.1) the terms in ψ^2 are seen to represent the information on the parameters provided by the variance estimates. Now we have

$$\frac{1}{\sigma^2\phi^2} + 2\psi^2 = \frac{1}{\sigma^2\phi^2}\left\{1 + 2\left[\frac{d(\sigma\phi)}{d\eta}\right]^2\right\},$$

so that the contribution of the variance estimates to the information is proportional to

$$2 \left[\frac{d(\sigma\phi)}{d\eta} \right]^2 . \qquad (4.3)$$

In general, this quantity is small, and so the information may be ignored. For example, if

$$\phi = \eta,$$

then σ is usually a small fraction; the quantity (4.3) is then $2\sigma^2 \ll 1$.

For this reason, and also for computational simplicity, the least-squares equations rather than the maximum-likelihood equations are generally used. Even for these, some iteration is required, since the weights must be determined approximately from preliminary estimates of the expected values. Only two cycles of iteration are usually required, however, since great accuracy in the weights is not necessary for giving accurate estimates of means and regression coefficients.

4.6 ESTIMATION BY THE METHOD OF MAXIMUM LIKELIHOOD IN GENERAL

As mentioned in Section 4.5, statistical parameters may be efficiently estimated in general by the method of maximum likelihood, which provides not only the required estimates but also their estimated variances and covariances. The method is in most cases difficult to apply directly, but the equations may usually be solved expeditiously by iterative means.

Although a detailed discussion of the method of maximum likelihood is beyond the scope of this book, it is of interest to see how it links up with regression methods in general. If L is the logarithm of the likelihood of a sample of independent observations, we have

$$L = S(l)$$

where the l are the log likelihoods of the members of the sample. If L is a function of parameters $\theta_1, \theta_2, \cdots$, it is differentiated with respect to each of these parameters, and the derivatives are equated to zero, to give equations for estimates of these parameters. The equations may be written

$$\frac{\partial L}{\partial \theta_i} \equiv S \frac{\partial l}{\partial \theta_i} = 0 \qquad (i = 1, 2, \cdots)$$

or

$$S(l_i) = 0.$$

If trial values of these estimates are chosen, improved values may be determined by successive approximation. The equations for the adjustments e_i are

$$e_1 S(l_1{}^2) + e_2 S(l_1 l_2) + \cdots = S(l_1)$$

or generally

$$\sum_h e_h S(l_h l_i) = S(l_i).$$

The equations show that, formally, the e_i may be regarded as regression coefficients for the regression of 1 on the l_i. In exactly the same way as in ordinary regression analysis, the variances and covariances are given by the elements of the inverse of the matrix of the $S(l_h l_i)$.

This presentation is actually a slight modification of the method as usually presented; usually the expected values of the sums of squares and products $S(l_h l_i)$ are given rather than the sample values. There is theoretically little to choose between the two methods, although use of expected values may reduce the calculations a little. Sample values have been used here to show the relationship to ordinary regression analysis.

CHAPTER 5

Choice among
Regression Formulas

5.1 GENERAL

In previous chapters we have considered the fitting of regression equations, simple or multiple, based on a given set of independent variables and assuming a given form of relationship. However, it very often happens that the experimenter is faced with a choice of two or more possible regression functions. We shall consider in this chapter how different independent variables and forms of regression functions may be compared.

There are several variants of the problem. First of all, there may be two or more independent variables (or sets of them), on which the regression of the dependent variable may be calculated. To test the significance of differences between different independent variables, some work of Hotelling (1940) is useful. A second type of problem is one in which a least-squares regression on a set of variables is to be compared with a theoretical formula based on the same or different variables. In the third type two or more theoretical formulas are compared; Hoel (1947) and Williams and Kloot (1953) have given some results for this type of problem.

Since each variant introduces different logical problems, each will be considered separately. It should be borne in mind that, in comparing different regression equations or theoretical formulas, the exact logical basis of the test should be made quite explicit; otherwise there is the risk of making erroneous deductions.

We have already considered one problem of choice among regression formulas in Chapter 3, in providing tests of significance in multiple regression. For in testing the significance of the contribution of any variable to the regression, we are enabling a decision to be made whether or not that variable is worth including in the equation. Of course, as previously emphasized, the decision may be made on grounds other than that of a significance test; but a test provides a basis for a decision when no other basis is given. As the test of significance of a regression coefficient is a straightforward application of the usual procedures of the analysis of variance, it will not be considered further here.

5.2 COMPARISON OF TWO OR MORE INDEPENDENT VARIABLES

When two or more independent variables are measured, it will generally be appropriate to calculate a regression equation including such variables as contribute significantly to the relationship. However, occasions arise when the choice of one only is to be made, either for reasons of economy in subsequent investigations, or because the additional contribution of more than one variable is not expected to be important. In such cases it is desirable to have a test whether the sums of squares for regression on different independent variables are significantly different.

The test developed by Hotelling depends on the fact that the sum of squares for regression of y on x_i is the square of a linear function of y. His test is of the null hypothesis that these linear functions all have the same expectation.

We may write

$$z_i = Sy(x_i - \bar{x}_i)/\sqrt{S(x_i - \bar{x}_i)^2}$$
$$= p_i/\sqrt{t_{ii}}$$

for the square root of the sum of squares for the regression of y on x_i. Then the variances and covariances of the z_i in terms of the residual variance σ^2 are as follows:

$$V(z_i) = \sigma^2,$$
$$\text{Cov}\,(z_h, z_i) = r_{hi}\sigma^2,$$

where r_{hi} is the sample correlation coefficient of x_h and x_i.

Now let the elements of the inverse of the correlation matrix (r_{hi}) be denoted by r^{hi}. Then the mean of the z_i is given by

$$z = \sum_h \sum_i r^{hi} z_i / \sum_h \sum_i r^{hi}$$

and the sum of squares of deviations of the z_i from their mean is therefore

$$\sum_h \sum_i r^{hi} z_h z_i - \frac{(\sum_h \sum_i r^{hi} z_i)^2}{\sum_h \sum_i r^{hi}}$$
$$= \sum_h \sum_i r^{hi} z_h z_i - z^2 \sum_h \sum_i r^{hi}.$$

This sum of squares provides a criterion for the reality of differences among the z_i, and consequently for the differences among the x_i as predictors for y. It may be tested against the residual mean square from the multiple regression of y on the x_i. The test criterion thus has an F distribution with $p-1$ and $n-p-1$ degrees of freedom.

For demonstrating algebraically the method of arriving at the significance test, this derivation is satisfactory, but for calculation purposes some modifications may be introduced to simplify the work. Rather than calculating the inverse of the matrix (r_{hi}), it is preferable to invert the matrix (t_{hi}) of sums of squares and products of the x_i. This has the advantage of avoiding the calculation of the correlation coefficients and the square roots involved therein; also, the inverse of (t_{hi}) is required in calculating the multiple regression equation and the sum of squares for regression, and so has to be calculated in any case. Then, if the elements of the inverse of (t_{hi}) are designated t^{hi}, we have

$$r^{hi} = t^{hi}\sqrt{(t_{hh}t_{ii})}.$$

Hence

$$\sum_h\sum_i r^{hi}z_h z_i = \sum_h\sum_i t^{hi}p_h p_i = \sum_i b_i p_i,$$

which is recognizable as the sum of squares for regression, with p degrees of freedom.

The quantity z is a little more troublesome. We have

$$\sum_h\sum_i r^{hi}z_i = \sum_h\sqrt{t_{hh}}\sum_i t^{hi}p_i = \sum_h\sqrt{t_{hh}}\, b_h,$$

which is simply a weighted sum of the regression coefficients.

$$\sum_h\sum_i r^{hi} = \sum_h\sqrt{t_{hh}}\sum_i t^{hi}\sqrt{t_{ii}}$$

and so is the most troublesome factor to calculate.

From this derivation it is seen that the test of significance proposed by Hotelling is equivalent to a test of the adequacy of a single compound variate $\sum_h\sum_i \sqrt{t_{hh}}\, t^{hi}x_i$ as a regression function to replace the multiple regression function. The regression sum of squares corresponding to this variate is $z^2\sum_h\sum_i r^{hi}$; the variate is so constructed that it will agree with the multiple regression function provided each of the variables x_i is equally highly correlated with y.

5.3   EXAMPLE

Example 5.1   The Comparison of Two Independent Variables for Estimating Maximum Compressive Strength. The most useful applications of this test are in the comparison of two independent variables. The following example is taken from some tests carried out to determine the relation between maximum compressive strength parallel to the grain (y) and density (x_1) for radiata pine. Since some specimens of radiata pine contain a large amount of resin which contributes to the density but contributes little to the strength, the resin content of the specimens was determined and an adjusted density figure (x_2) calculated. The question arose whether the correlation of y with x_2 was significantly higher than that with x_1. The data for this experiment are shown in Table 5.1.

TABLE 5.1

VALUES OF MAXIMUM COMPRESSIVE STRENGTH (y), DENSITY (x_1),
AND ADJUSTED DENSITY (x_2) FOR 42 SPECIMENS OF
PINUS RADIATA

Maximum Compressive Strength, y, lb./sq. in.	Density, x_1, lb./cu. ft.	Adjusted Density, x_2, lb./cu. ft.	Maximum Compressive Strength, y, lb./sq. in.	Density, x_1, lb./cu. ft.	Adjusted Density, x_2, lb./cu. ft.
3040	29.2	25.4	3840	30.7	30.7
2470	24.7	22.2	3800	32.7	32.6
3610	32.3	32.2	4600	32.6	32.5
3480	31.3	31.0	1900	22.1	20.8
3810	31.5	30.9	2530	25.3	23.1
2330	24.5	23.9	2920	30.8	29.8
1800	19.9	19.2	4990	38.9	38.1
3110	27.3	27.2	1670	22.1	21.3
3160	27.1	26.3	3310	29.2	28.5
2310	24.0	23.9	3450	30.1	29.2
4360	33.8	33.2	3600	31.4	31.4
1880	21.5	21.0	2850	26.7	25.9
3670	32.2	29.0	1590	22.1	21.4
1740	22.5	22.0	3770	30.3	29.8
2250	27.5	23.8	3850	32.0	30.6
2650	25.6	25.3	2480	23.2	22.6
4970	34.5	34.2	3570	30.3	30.3
2620	26.2	25.7	2620	29.9	23.8
2900	26.7	26.4	1890	20.8	18.4
1670	21.1	20.0	3030	33.2	29.4
2540	24.1	23.9	3030	28.2	28.2

The analysis shows that (as was to be expected) the adjusted density gives the higher sum of squares for regression. Tables 5.2 and 5.3 and the accompanying calculations show the derivation of the quantity z. The analysis of variance (Table 5.4) shows the sum of squares for regression and its partition into two parts, the second providing the test for difference of correlations. It is seen that the sum of squares for difference of correlations is not significant, the value of F being 3.20. However, this is a test of departure from the null hypothesis in either direction. If, as seems reasonable, we are interested only in departures giving adjusted density the greater correlation, a one-tailed t test on the difference would be appropriate. This is equivalent to doubling the probability deemed significant on the F test. As the F value of 3.20, corresponding to a t value of 1.79, is significant at the 10 per cent point, the difference may be taken as significant at the 5 per cent point.

TABLE 5.2

SUMS OF SQUARES AND PRODUCTS OF VALUES IN TABLE 5.1

	x_1	x_2	y	Sums of Squares for Simple Regression
x_1	828.24	820.79	152,854	28,209,600
x_2	820.79	885.58	162,304	29,746,100

TABLE 5.3

THE INVERSE MATRIX AND THE PARTIAL REGRESSION COEFFICIENTS

$$10^{-6} \times \begin{bmatrix} 14{,}814.84 & -13{,}730.97 \\ -13{,}730.97 & 13{,}855.60 \end{bmatrix} \quad \begin{matrix} b_i \\ 35.916 \\ 149.986 \end{matrix}$$

$$\sum_h \sqrt{t_{hh}}\, b_h = 5497.021$$

$$\sum_h \sum_i \sqrt{(t_{hh} t_{ii})}\, t^{hi} = 1.021\ 249$$

Sum of squares for regression on compound variable

$$= 5497.021^2 / 1.021\ 249$$
$$= 29{,}588{,}500$$

TABLE 5.4

ANALYSIS OF VARIANCE FOR COMPARING CORRELATIONS

	D.F.	Sum of Squares	Mean Square
Regression on compound variable	1	29,588,500	
Difference of correlations	1	244,700	244,700
Regression on x_1 and x_2	2	29,833,200	
Residual	39	2,979,200	76,390
Total	41	32,812,400	

5.4 A SPECIAL CASE: TEST OF SIGNIFICANCE OF REGRESSION THROUGH ORIGIN

There are numerous special applications and adaptations of Hotelling's test. One of the more important is in testing the significance of a regression through the origin. If a regression of the form

$$Y = b_1 x_1 \tag{5.1}$$

is fitted to a set of data, the fact that the line passes through the origin results in b_1's having a small standard error. However, the standard error of b_1 does not provide the test of significance that is generally required. What is required is not a test whether b_1 differs significantly from zero but a test whether the relationship (5.1) accounts for the variation in y significantly better than the assumption that Y is constant; that is, the alternative regression

$$Y = b_0 x_0,$$

where

$$x_0 = 1,$$

so that

$$b_0 = \bar{y}.$$

Hotelling's test is directly applicable here, since there is a choice of two alternative independent variables, x_0 and x_1. The result is an F test with 1 and $n - 2$ degrees of freedom, which may be shown to reduce to the form

$$F = \frac{\left(Sy x_1 - Sy \sqrt{\dfrac{Sx_1^2}{n}}\right)^2}{2\left(Sx_1^2 - Sx_1 \sqrt{\dfrac{Sx_1^2}{n}}\right)s^2},$$

where s^2 is the residual mean square of y, with $n - 2$ degrees of freedom.

Example 5.2 Significance of Regression through Origin. Good examples of a test of significance of a regression through the origin are not easy to find; for if such a regression is indicated, it is in most cases highly significant, and no test is necessary. The significance of a regression through the origin would be required with data consisting of a cluster of points at some distance from the origin, as in the following hypothetical set of data (Table 5.5).

For these data we find the regression coefficient for the line through the origin to be

$$b_1 = 11{,}243/955$$
$$= 11.77$$

with standard error

$$\sqrt{\left(\frac{133{,}772 - 11{,}243^2/955}{5 \times 955}\right)}$$
$$= 0.54.$$

The ratio of b_1 to its standard error is highly significant. However, to test the significance of b_1 in the manner described, we determine the residual mean square (with four degrees of freedom)

$$\tfrac{1}{4}(5876 - 293^2/17.5) = 242.6$$

and then calculate

$$F = \frac{[11,243 - 876\sqrt{(955/6)}]^2}{2[955 - 75\sqrt{(955/6)}]\,242.6}$$

$$= 8.58,$$

which is significant at the 5 per cent level.

The result of this significance test shows that it is clearly more appropriate than the simple test of the departure of b_1 from zero.

TABLE 5.5

HYPOTHETICAL DATA ILLUSTRATING TEST FOR SIGNIFICANCE
OF REGRESSION THROUGH ORIGIN

| | | | | | | | Total | Sums of Squares and Products | |
								Uncorrected	Corrected
x_1	10	11	12	13	14	15	75	955	17.5
y	109	134	123	134	179	197	876	133,772	5876
						Sx_1y		11,243	293

5.5   GENERALIZATION OF HOTELLING'S TEST

The test of significance described in previous paragraphs can readily be generalized to multiple regressions in which a set of independent variables has been decided on and the choice of one of a number of additional variables is to be made. The test is then based on the comparison of the sums of squares for partial regression on each of the new variables, and no new principle is involved. If there are q variables in the equation, and one more out of p new variables is to be decided on, the significance will be tested by means of an F with $p - 1$ and $n - p - q - 1$ degrees of freedom.

Since the test is based on the comparison of the square roots of regression sums of squares, it will be seen that it cannot be generalized for the comparing of sets of two or more variables. The square root of a sum of squares for one degree of freedom is a linear function of y; the comparison of such linear functions is amenable to analysis of variance techniques. A sum of squares with two or more degrees of freedom, on the other hand, cannot be treated in this way, so that no generalization is possible.

5.6 COMMENTS ON THE TEST

The limitations of this test should be noted. In the first place, it is strictly a conditional test. It is valid for comparing the efficiency, as predictors, of the given sets of values of the independent variables, without reference to any population from which they might have been drawn. It cannot, however, validly be extended to drawing conclusions about future observed values of the independent variables.

In a few applications it may be reasonable to assume that the independent variables are fixed and that the conditional test is all that is required. In other applications it will be found that the test, although not exact, is a good approximation. In general, however, if a test of the efficiency of predictors for future use is required, some allowance will have to be made for the variation of the values from those observed. This question has not received much attention. An approximate test has been derived for comparing two predictors, when the variables are assumed drawn from a normal population. The test criterion, distributed approximately as F with 1 and $n-3$ degrees of freedom, is

$$\frac{(z_1 - z_2)^2}{2s^2(1 - r_{12}) + \dfrac{(z_1 + z_2)^2(1 - r_{12})^3}{4(n-1)(1 + r_{12})}}$$

where s^2 is the residual mean square from the regression. This may be compared with the criterion given by Hotelling's test, namely

$$\frac{(z_1 - z_2)^2}{2s^2(1 - r_{12})}.$$

The additional term in the denominator of the first expression makes allowance for the variation in the x_i.

Thus, in Example 5.1, if the wider hypothesis is being tested, we have

$$z_1 = \sqrt{28{,}209{,}600} = 5311.3$$
$$z_2 = \sqrt{29{,}746{,}100} = 5454.0$$
$$r_{12} = 0.95839$$

and the test criterion becomes

$$\frac{(5311.3 - 5454.0)^2}{2 \times 76{,}390 \times 0.04161 + \dfrac{10{,}765.3^2 \times 0.04161^3}{4 \times 41 \times 1.95839}}$$
$$= \frac{142.7^2}{6357 + 26}$$
$$= 3.19.$$

The difference between this result and that given previously is negligible, probably because of the large value of r_{12} for this example.

If the ratio of the variances is known, we may make an exact test to compare two predictors. The test, when the variances are equal, is equivalent to testing the difference of the partial regression coefficients. Thus

$$F = \frac{(b_1 - b_2)^2}{(t^{11} - 2t^{12} + t^{22})s^2}$$

with 1 and $n - 3$ degrees of freedom. Since both the predictors in Example 5.1 are densities, it may be reasonable to assume that the variances are equal. Applying the test based on that assumption, we find

$$F = \frac{(35.916 - 149.986)^2 \times 10^6}{56{,}132.38 \times 76{,}390}$$

$$= 3.03.$$

Here, too, the result differs little from that of the original test ($F = 3.20$).

It should be remarked that, for a strictly valid application of Hotelling's test, the sign of the regression coefficient should be taken into account. That is to say, the test is not one of the absolute value of the correlation but of its actual value. Fortunately, when the test is to be applied, there is usually prior knowledge of whether each regression coefficient is positive or negative, and the null hypothesis can be framed accordingly. Thus, in Example 5.1 comparing density and adjusted density, the two regression coefficients are known to be positive. If the regressions of y on, say, x and x^{-1} were being compared, the two coefficients would be expected to be opposite in sign, and the null hypothesis would be framed in terms of the regressions on x and $-x^{-1}$. Occasionally, however, there will be no prior reason to assume that the coefficients are either positive or negative; to take them all as positive will then bias the test, making the significance conservative. It would be valid to allot signs at random; however, the significance attained would not then necessarily be attributable to difference in correlation, but might be partly attributable to difference in sign. In other words, the null hypothesis we should like to test would be that the absolute values of the correlations are equal; all that Hotelling's test can do is to test the null hypothesis that their actual values are equal. In most practical cases, of course, this limitation is not a serious one, for the null hypothesis can be framed in the light of the expected direction of the regression.

5.7 COMPARISON OF A THEORETICAL AND A LEAST-SQUARES FORMULA

The comparison of a theoretical and a least-squares formula is likely to be of practical interest only when the same independent variables are present in each, and only then can a satisfactory significance test be made. This problem has already been dealt with in Chapter 3 on multiple regression. If the hypothetical formula is

$$\eta = \beta_0 + \beta_1 x_1 + \cdots + \beta_p x_p$$

and the least-squares equation, based on the same variables x_i, is

$$Y = b_0 + b_1 x_1 + \cdots + b_p x_p,$$

the sum of squares of deviations of y from η can be split into two parts as follows:

$$S(y - \eta)^2 = S(y - Y)^2 + S(Y - \eta)^2$$

the degrees of freedom being

$$n = (n - p - 1) + (p + 1).$$

Hence, to test the improvement of Y over η (or, what is the same thing, the adequacy of η to represent the relationship), we have an F with $p + 1$ and $n - p - 1$ degrees of freedom:

$$F = \frac{(n - p - 1)S(Y - \eta)^2}{(p + 1)S(y - Y)^2}.$$

The totality of all sets of values β_i for which F calculated in this way is not significant provides the simultaneous fiducial range for the β_i.

5.8 COMPARISON OF TWO THEORETICAL FORMULAS

In comparing theoretical formulas it is easy to determine which of a number of formulas gives the best prediction in the least-square sense, but it is not easy to establish valid significance tests, since in fact each formula will correspond to a different null hypothesis. It will not always be possible to frame a null hypothesis which will enable a test between different formulas to be set up. It is interesting to note that Hoel (1947) and Williams and Kloot (1953) have both examined the comparison of two theoretical formulas, but they arrive at different results because they are testing different hypotheses.

Hoel considers the comparison of the original formula for the expected value of y with an alternative; we shall designate these f_1 and f_2 respectively.

The test he devises is whether the data are concordant with the assumption of f_1, or whether f_1 should be rejected in favor of f_2. As he says, the test "should not be interpreted as a device for selecting one of two alternative formulas"; the null hypothesis is in fact that f_1 is appropriate. Hoel arrives at the intuitively reasonable criterion, namely the regression of $y - f_1$ on $f_2 - f_1$. If this is significantly positive, then f_1 is to be rejected in favor of f_2.

Williams and Kloot's test is one of the null hypothesis that the two theoretical formulas are equal in ability to predict y. As might be expected, the test is symmetrical with respect to f_1 and f_2, reducing to that of the regression (through the origin) of $y - \frac{1}{2}(f_1 + f_2)$ on $f_2 - f_1$. A significant positive regression indicates that f_2 predicts better than f_1, a significant negative regression that f_1 predicts better than f_2. A non-significant regression leaves undecided the choice between f_1 and f_2.

These two alternative possible tests are applicable to different hypotheses, but the fact that such alternatives exist shows that the null hypothesis must be clearly defined before a test is made. For comparing more than two theoretical formulas, the situation is even more complicated.

Example 5.3   Comparison of Two Formulas for Estimating the Density of a Timber Specimen from That of Neighboring Specimens. The data used here are from the experiment discussed in Section 3.16, Example 3.5. Sets of five end-matched specimens are taken from a number of pieces of timber and the density determined on each. For purposes of subsequent experiments the density of the second and fourth specimens in each set must be estimated from that of the other three specimens. We denote the values for the alternate specimens by x_1, x_2, and x_3, and that for the specimen between x_1 and x_2 by y. Two alternative formulas are suggested for estimating y:

$$f_1 = \tfrac{1}{2}(x_1 + x_2)$$

or

$$f_2 = \tfrac{1}{3}(x_1 + x_2 + x_3).$$

The expression f_2 has the advantage of being based on more specimens and hence will be less affected by random variation; on the other hand, it will be biased by any linear trend in the density values along the material.

From a set of 228 results, the following results were obtained:

$$S(y - f_1)^2 = 110.7650$$
$$S(y - f_2)^2 = 127.1689,$$

showing that f_1 may be better than f_2.

The difference of these two residual sums of squares is

$$S(2y - f_1 - f_2)(f_1 - f_2) = 16.4039,$$

which is seen to be twice the sum of products of $y - \frac{1}{2}(f_1 + f_2)$ and $f_1 - f_2$. The sum of squares of $f_1 - f_2$ is

$$S(f_1 - f_2)^2 = 32.50,$$

so that the sum of squares for the regression of $y - \frac{1}{2}(f_1 + f_2)$ on $f_1 - f_2$ is

$$16.4039^2/4 \times 32.50 = 2.070.$$

As the residual mean square (obtained from the complete data) is 0.4275, we have

$$F = 2.070/0.4275$$

$$= 4.84 \text{ (significant at the 5 per cent level)}.$$

Hence we may conclude that f_1 predicts more closely than f_2.

Note that for this example the symmetrical test has been applied. Had the formula f_1 been the established one, and the question of replacing it by f_2 been raised, Hoel's test would have been appropriate.

5.9 EXTENSION TO THE COMPARISON OF MORE THAN TWO THEORETICAL FORMULAS

We have seen that there are at least two different possible tests of significance for the comparison of two theoretical formulas, depending on the emphasis to be given to each formula. We have described the symmetrical test, in which each formula is on an equal footing, the comparison being directly on the goodness of fit of each, and an unsymmetrical test, wherein one formula is the accepted one and the question of its replacement by an alternative is considered. In the same way, for the comparison of three or more theoretical formulas, there are numerous possible tests; any test should be framed in the light of the emphasis being given initially to each formula. We shall consider here only a symmetrical test, into which each formula enters equally, none being regarded initially as established or accepted.

As Williams and Kloot have shown, the regression test just outlined for the comparison of two formulas is equivalent to a test of the significance of the difference between the residual sums of squares left by each formula. With more than two formulas it seems appropriate to frame the test as a test of the homogeneity of the residual sums of squares. Such a test, for correlated variables, has been developed by Wilks (1946). In this particular application the test simplifies greatly because, as is readily seen, the differences among the residual sums of squares are linear in the y values.

It must be pointed out that Wilks's test, or any other test of homogeneity of variances, is not strictly applicable here, since the different sums of squares are not actually variance estimates. If one formula is the "true" one, the sum of squares of departures from this formula is a variance estimate, but all the other sums of squares contain a systematic component resulting from differences between the formula applied and the true one. However, the formal application of Wilks's test to the homogeneity of these residual sums of squares gives some interesting results and confirms a significance test derived in an intuitive manner. Wilks's test criterion, with p formulas to be compared, is

$$\lambda = \frac{|v_{hi}|}{v^p(1-r)^{p-1}(1+\overline{p-1}r)} \tag{5.2}$$

where*
$$v_{hi} = S(y-f_h)(y-f_i) = u - p_h - p_i + t_{hi} \text{ (say)},$$

$$pv = \sum_i v_{ii}$$

$$= pS(y^2) - 2\sum_i S(yf_i) + \sum_i S(f_i^2)$$

$$= pu - 2\sum_i p_i + \sum_i t_{ii},$$

$$r = \frac{\sum_{h \neq i}\sum v_{hi}}{(p-1)\sum_i v_{ii}}.$$

Both numerator and denominator are of the second degree in y.

The numerator is found to be proportional to the sum of squares of residuals from the least-squares combination

$$f^* = b_1'f_1 + b_2'f_2 + \cdots + b_p'f_p,$$

where the b_i' are subject to the restriction

$$\sum_i b_i' = 1;$$

in fact, the numerator

$$|v_{hi}| = S(y-f^*)^2|t_{hi}|\sum_h\sum_i t^{hi}.$$

The sum of squares in this expression for the numerator has $n-p+1$ degrees of freedom.

Now

$$v(1-r) = \frac{1}{p(p-1)}[(p-1)\sum_i v_{ii} - \sum_{h \neq i}\sum v_{hi}]$$

$$= \frac{1}{p(p-1)}[(p-1)\sum_i t_{ii} - \sum_{h \neq i}\sum t_{hi}]$$

$$= \frac{1}{p-1}S[\sum_i f_i^2 - (\sum_i f_i)^2/p]$$

$$= \frac{1}{p-1} \times \text{the sum of squares between the } f\text{'s, within} \\ \text{samples, with } n(p-1) \text{ degrees of freedom.}$$

This term is, however, independent of the y.

Also

$$v(1 + \overline{p - 1}r) = \frac{1}{p}(\sum_i v_{ii} + \sum\sum_{h \neq i} v_{hi})$$

$$= \frac{1}{p} S[\sum_h (y - f_h)]^2$$

$$= pS(y - \bar{f})^2$$

where
$$\bar{f} = (f_1 + f_2 + \cdots + f_p)/p.$$

This sum of squares has n degrees of freedom.

Thus, apart from factors independent of y, the criterion (5.2) is the ratio

$$S(y - f^*)^2/S(y - \bar{f})^2.$$

The numerator measures departure from the compound formula f^*, so chosen that each formula contributes to it according to its fitness as an estimate of y; in the denominator the departure is from an average formula, to which each original formula contributes equally. The ratio appears intuitively to provide a satisfactory test criterion. It may be tested by means of an F test:

$$F = \frac{n - p + 1}{p - 1} \frac{S(y - \bar{f})^2 - S(y - f^*)^2}{S(y - f^*)^2}$$

with $p - 1$ and $n - p + 1$ degrees of freedom.

Before going on to consider the best methods of calculating these sums of squares, we shall look at the other factors, not involving y, in Wilks's criterion. These are

$$\frac{|t_{hi}| \sum_h \sum_i t^{hi}}{\left[\frac{1}{p(p-1)}(p\sum_i t_{ii} - \sum_h \sum_i t_{hi})\right]^{p-1}}.$$

The greater the variation among the f_i within samples, the smaller, and hence the more highly significant, this ratio will be. It is a measure of the consistency of the different formulas among themselves. It can, however, be ignored for present purposes, since, first, the quantities involved are fixed variables and so do not generate a distribution, and second, because it does not add to the information already provided by the proposed test criterion, on the concordance of the different formulas with the observed data.

In order to apply the test we need to calculate both the sums of squares of departures and the regression coefficients (subject to the restriction mentioned). These are best determined indirectly, and the following steps are found suitable.

We work with the v_{hi}, the sums of squares and products of the departures. The sum of squares of departure from $\bar{f}$ is simply the arithmetic mean of all the v_{hi}:

$$S(y - \bar{f})^2 = \frac{1}{p^2} \sum_h \sum_i v_{hi}.$$

The sum of squares of departures from f^* is

$$\sum_h \sum_i b_h' b_i' v_{hi}$$

the b_i' being subject to the restriction $\Sigma b_i' = 1$, and so chosen that the quadratic form is a minimum. Then it is found that

$$b_i' = \sum_h v^{hi} / \sum_h \sum_i v^{hi}$$

where the v^{hi} are the elements of the inverse of the matrix (v_{hi}).

The sum of squares of departures from f^* is then

$$1 / \sum_h \sum_i v^{hi},$$

with $n - p + 1$ degrees of freedom.

For comparing the regression coefficients b_i', the variances and covariances are given by formulas such as

$$V(b_1') = \sigma^2[v^{11} - (\sum_h v^{h1})^2 / \sum_h \sum_i v^{hi}]$$

$$= \sigma^2(v^{11} - b_1'^2 \sum_h \sum_i v^{hi})$$

and 　　　$$\mathrm{Cov}\,(b_1', b_2') = \sigma^2(v^{12} - \sum_h v^{h1} \sum_h v^{h2} / \sum_h \sum_i v^{hi})$$

$$= \sigma^2(v^{12} - b_1' b_2' \sum_h \sum_i v^{hi}).$$

Thus, the estimated covariance of b_1' and b_2' is

$$\frac{v^{12} - \sum_h v^{h1} \sum_h v^{h2} / \sum_h \sum_i v^{hi}}{(n - p + 1)\sum_h \sum_i v^{hi}} = \frac{1}{(n - p + 1)} \left[\frac{v^{12}}{\sum_h \sum_i v^{hi}} - b_1' b_2' \right].$$

Example 5.4 Comparison of Three Theoretical Formulas for Estimating the Ultimate Failing Strength of Eccentrically Loaded Columns. A number of theoretical formulas have been derived for estimating the failing load of columns from knowledge of the eccentricity of the load, the slenderness ratio of the column, and the strength properties of the material. In Table 5.6 are set out a series of results given by direct test (y), and by three different formulas (f_1, f_2, and f_3), for specimens of timber of silver quandong (*Elaeocarpus grandis* F.v.M.). Table 5.7 gives the required sums of squares and products (uncorrected), and Table 5.8 the sums of squares and

TABLE 5.6

OBSERVED AND ESTIMATED FAILING LOADS FOR 33 COLUMNS OF SILVER QUANDONG, LOADED AT NOMINAL ECCENTRICITY 1/120

y Test P_u/f_c	f_1 P_{se}/f_c	f_2 Estimated P_{pe}/f_c	f_3 P_{je}/f_c
0.434	0.443	0.410	0.467
0.433	0.431	0.388	0.461
0.475	0.454	0.411	0.483
0.432	0.414	0.366	0.449
0.312	0.308	0.288	0.314
0.315	0.310	0.285	0.321
0.310	0.307	0.282	0.318
0.326	0.321	0.295	0.334
0.296	0.297	0.268	0.312
0.311	0.301	0.274	0.315
0.217	0.224	0.208	0.228
0.250	0.247	0.228	0.254
0.241	0.232	0.217	0.235
0.246	0.244	0.228	0.248
0.260	0.249	0.228	0.256
0.256	0.245	0.227	0.250
0.167	0.166	0.157	0.167
0.171	0.170	0.159	0.171
0.175	0.172	0.161	0.173
0.184	0.178	0.167	0.179
0.171	0.169	0.158	0.169
0.124	0.124	0.119	0.123
0.111	0.113	0.110	0.112
0.116	0.116	0.112	0.115
0.107	0.110	0.106	0.109
0.114	0.116	0.113	0.115
0.113	0.119	0.115	0.118
0.065	0.068	0.066	0.066
0.069	0.069	0.066	0.067
0.068	0.068	0.066	0.067
0.071	0.072	0.069	0.070
0.063	0.065	0.063	0.064
0.069	0.071	0.068	0.069

TABLE 5.7

SUMS OF SQUARES AND PRODUCTS (UNCORRECTED) OF
RESULTS IN TABLE 5.6

f_1	f_2	f_3	y
1.929 219	1.771 904	2.008 474	1.958 492
1.771 904	1.628 134	1.843 793	1.798 355
2.008 474	1.843 793	2.092 331	2.039 330
			1.989 298

TABLE 5.8

SUMS OF SQUARES AND PRODUCTS OF DEPARTURES FROM
THEORETICAL FORMULAS

$$10^{-6} \times \begin{bmatrix} 1,533 & 4,355 & -50 \\ 4,355 & 20,722 & -4,594 \\ -50 & -4,594 & 2,969 \end{bmatrix}$$

Sum of elements $= 24,646 \times 10^{-6}$

Sum of squares for departure from $\bar{f}$

$$= 24,646 \times 10^{-6}/9$$
$$= 2,738.4 \times 10^{-6}$$

products, v_{hi}, for discrepancies from the different formulas. These figures indicate that f_1 and f_3 are superior to f_2 as estimates of y, but that there may be little to choose between f_1 and f_3. In practice, f_1 would be used unless an alternative were chosen for reasons of consistency or convenience.

In Table 5.9 the inverse matrix and the regression coefficients are determined. Inspection of the regression coefficients confirms that f_1 is the most, and f_2 the least, satisfactory formula. Table 5.10 gives the adjusted inverse matrix from which the variances and covariances of the regression coefficients may be found. The over-all differences between the formulas are seen, from the analysis of

TABLE 5.9

INVERSE MATRIX AND REGRESSION COEFFICIENTS

			Sum	b_i'
5317.74	−1670.93	−2495.91	1150.90	1.083 16
−1670.93	598.49	897.92	−174.52	−0.164 25
−2495.91	897.92	1684.15	86.16	0.081 09
			1062.54	1.000 00

Sum of squares for departure from f^*

$$= 1/1062.54$$
$$= 941.1 \times 10^{-6}$$

TABLE 5.10

ADJUSTED INVERSE MATRIX $(v^{hi} - b_i' \sum_k v^{hk})$

$$\begin{bmatrix} 4071.13 & -1481.90 & -2589.23 \\ -1481.90 & 569.83 & 912.07 \\ -2589.23 & 912.07 & 1677.16 \end{bmatrix}$$

TABLE 5.11

ANALYSIS OF VARIANCE

	D.F.	Sum of Squares ($\times 10^6$)	Mean Square ($\times 10^6$)
Difference of regressions	2	1797.3	899**
Departure from f^*	31	941.1	30.36
Departure from f	33	2738.4	

** Significant at 1 per cent level

variance, Table 5.11, to be significant at the 1 per cent level. To test the difference between f_2 and f_3, for example, we have

$$b_2' - b_3' = -0.24534$$
$$V(b_2' - b_3') = 30.36 \,(569.83 - 2 \times 912.07 + 1677.16) \times 10^{-6}$$
$$= 0.012\ 838,$$

so that
$$F = (-0.24534)^2/0.012\ 838$$
$$= 4.69, \text{ significant at the 5 per cent level.}$$

CHAPTER 6

Estimation from
the Regression Equation

6.1 USE OF INFORMATION FROM REGRESSION
RELATIONSHIPS

The ultimate purpose of most determinations of regression equations is to use them to derive estimates; either estimates of the dependent variable from values of the independent variables (direct estimation), of one of the independent variables, given values of all the others (inverse estimation), or determination of the regression coefficients themselves, as constants of proportionality measuring the observable effect of one variable on another. It is therefore important not only that the regression equation be correctly determined but also that the correct method of estimation be applied. This chapter therefore discusses how correct estimates should·be made, some of the difficulties arising in deriving estimates, and some applications.

It has been thought worthwhile to lay considerable stress on the need for correct methods of estimation, because there appears to be considerable confusion on the subject, even in the statistical literature. It is believed that there should be no difficulty in resolving a particular problem provided the actual setup of the data is borne in mind and the purpose for which the results are to be used is clear. These points will be amplified later.

One point on which there is sometimes uncertainty is the regression equation to be employed, that is, which variable is to be treated as the dependent variable. It must first be emphasized that the dependent variable has to be subject to random error in order that the theory on which the method of estimation of the regression equation rests may be applicable; a variable which is errorless, or which has been subject to selection (even though also subject to error) cannot be chosen as dependent variable. For example, in the calibration of electrical moisture meters timber has to be conditioned to equilibrium moisture content under a number of different temperature and humidity conditions and its electrical resistance determined. Then, since moisture content has been selected

90

(even though subject to considerable variation at any one condition), it must be taken as the independent variable. The regression of resistance on moisture content will be determined, even though, in using the equation, moisture content will be estimated from electrical resistance.

On the other hand, if the variable to be estimated from the equation is subject to random error and has not been subject to selection, it should be used as the dependent variable. In particular, when both variables are subject to error, in simple regression, either regression equation may be used, depending on which variable is to be predicted. The many problems in which it is not possible to do this—especially in calibration experiments and the like—give rise to the device of inverse estimation from the regression equation.

6.2 THE INTERPRETATION OF FIDUCIAL STATEMENTS ABOUT A PARAMETER

In this chapter we shall be deriving fiducial statements about the values of parameters. The interpretation of these statements, which has already been discussed in Section 1.9, is fairly clear in simple problems. There are, however, a number of points that need to be considered carefully in less straightforward applications.

To begin with, a fiducial statement about a parameter is, broadly speaking, a statement that the parameter lies in a certain range or takes a certain set of values. The statement is either true or false in any particular instance, but it is made according to a rule which ensures that such statements, when applied in repeated sampling, have a given probability (say, 0.95 or 0.99) of being correct. The familiar example is that of setting limits to the mean of a normal population. If $\bar{y}$ is the mean and s the standard deviation of a sample of n from a normal population with mean η, the t distribution enables us to determine a value of t such that, with probability $1 - P$, $\bar{y}$ lies within the range given by the inequality

$$\eta - ts/\sqrt{n} < \bar{y} < \eta + ts/\sqrt{n}. \qquad (6.1)$$

The equivalent statement about η, namely

$$\bar{y} - ts/\sqrt{n} < \eta < \bar{y} + ts/\sqrt{n},$$

may be made with fiducial probability $1 - P$.

It is seen from this example that any statement of fiducial probability must be based on a direct probability statement (such as 6.1) about statistics derived from a sample; consequently, the two statements are equivalent, being but different ways of saying the same thing. This equivalence is clear enough in simple examples such as the one just given.

It appears necessary, however, to consider specifically a slightly more complicated case in which confusion has arisen.

The case is that of the estimation of a ratio. Suppose that x_1 and x_2 are two variables, the ratio of whose means is assumed to be γ. Then $\xi = x_1 - \gamma x_2$ is a variable with zero mean; we assume that ξ is normally distributed with unknown variance.

If γ is given, the mean and variance of ξ for any sample may be calculated and the departure of the mean from zero tested. In terms of x_1 and x_2, the mean of a sample of n will be

$$\bar{x}_1 - \gamma \bar{x}_2,$$

and the estimated variance of the mean will be

$$(t_{11} - 2\gamma t_{12} + \gamma^2 t_{22})/n(n - 1).$$

Accordingly, if F represents the tabular value of the F distribution with 1 and $n - 1$ degrees of freedom at probability level P, the inequality

$$(\bar{x}_1 - \gamma \bar{x}_2)^2 < F(t_{11} - 2\gamma t_{12} + \gamma^2 t_{22})/n(n - 1) \qquad (6.2)$$

is satisfied with probability $1 - P$. When γ is known, this result follows from ordinary probability theory; it is still true, although not experimentally verifiable, when γ is not known. If, however, the sample values are given but not γ, the inequality (6.2) defines a range of values for γ corresponding to a fiducial probability $1 - P$. This range will vary from sample to sample, both in position and extent; it differs from the fiducial range given by the simpler example in that, for certain values of the sample statistics, it will be unlimited, admitting all real values of γ. Nevertheless, in repeated sampling the various ranges given by (6.2) include γ with probability $1 - P$; this is apparent when it is seen that a statement about a range for γ is equivalent to a direct probability statement about ξ (or $\bar{x}_1 - \gamma \bar{x}_2$).

There is always a finite probability of occurrence of an unlimited fiducial range for γ, however large the sample may be. The interpretation of the unlimited range thus given by some samples is what needs to be clarified. If (6.2) is replaced by an equality and solved for γ, its two roots, when real, give fiducial limits for γ. When the roots are complex, the correct interpretation is that the sample puts no limitation on the value of γ. It has, however, sometimes been mistakenly assumed that γ has some "fiducial distribution," which in such cases can include complex values. By referring back to the original inequality (6.2), which clearly involves real x_1 and x_2 and hence only real values of γ, we see that this conclusion is incorrect.

We may deduce further facts about the fiducial limits for γ defined by the inequality (6.2). The larger the sample and the more accurately determined the means, the smaller will be the proportion of samples setting no limitation on γ, but there will always be a chance of such samples occurring. Now, clearly, γ is certain to lie in an unlimited range, so that, for the set of samples putting no limitation on γ, the fiducial probability is not $1 - P$ but 1. Since the over-all fiducial probability for all possible samples is $1 - P$, it follows that, for the samples imposing some limitation on γ, the fiducial probability must be less than $1 - P$. This result has been established rigorously elsewhere (Neyman, 1954). However, provided the experimenter applies the rule consistently for a given fiducial probability, the limits he obtains will correspond to the correct probability.

The following points about these fiducial limits may be noted.

(i) When $\bar{x}_1$ does not differ significantly from zero (i.e., when $\bar{x}_1{}^2 < Ft_{11}/n(n-1)$), the range for γ includes zero.

(ii) Similarly, when $\bar{x}_2$ does not differ significantly from zero (i.e., when $\bar{x}_2{}^2 < Ft_{22}/n(n-1)$), the range includes infinity, although it excludes a finite range of values (such a range is sometimes termed *exclusive*).

(iii) When $\bar{x}_1{}^2 t^{11} + 2\bar{x}_1\bar{x}_2 t^{12} + \bar{x}_2{}^2 t^{22} < F/n(n-1)$, the range for γ is unlimited. These points are brought out in the diagram (Figure 6.1).

Fiducial limits of this kind will occur from time to time throughout this book. For instance, when the position of the maximum or minimum of a fitted parabola is being determined (Section 6.11), we require the ratio of two regression coefficients; fiducial limits for the position of the maximum or minimum are then found by a method similar to that just shown. When the fiducial limits do not exist, the simple interpretation is that there is no evidence for the existence of a maximum or minimum. When the fiducial limits include infinity (case (ii)), this implies also that the extreme value may be either a maximum or a minimum, that is, that the curve is not a parabola and there is no evidence of departure from linearity. In this respect, the determination of fiducial limits will give the same verdict as a direct significance test on the parabolic regression coefficient. This is further discussed in Section 6.11.

Another instance is in testing the choice of the proportions in which two or more variables are included in a discriminant function, or in determining fiducial limits for these proportions. A discriminant function is a linear compound of two or more variables, chosen as a criterion to distinguish between different groups of individuals; for a discriminant function to be satisfactory, its sum of squares between groups for any sample must be a large fraction of the total sum of squares. The test for a given discriminant function will be discussed more fully in Chapter 10. It is analogous to the test for a ratio, in that it is a comparison between a mean square and a residual mean square, each of which is a polynomial

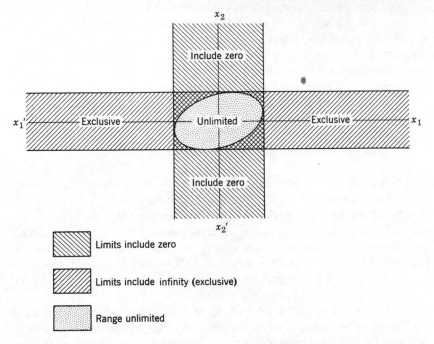

Figure 6.1. Fiducial limits for the ratio γ, corresponding to different values of $\bar{x}_1$ and $\bar{x}_2$, but with variances and covariance fixed.

function of the unknown parameter. Suppose that there are two variables, x_1 and x_2, and that the discriminant function under test is

$$\xi = x_1 + \gamma x_2.$$

The test is an application of the analysis of covariance (see Chapter 7). The regressions of x_1 on ξ, within and between groups, are determined, and their difference is tested for significance. A significant difference can be shown to indicate a value of γ which differs significantly from the optimum value, and is thus inconsistent with the data. It will often happen that to no value of γ does there correspond a significant difference, so that all values of γ are consistent with the data, and any linear function of x_1 and x_2 is a satisfactory discriminant function.

6.3   FIDUCIAL LIMITS

In direct estimation from a regression equation, the values of Y and its standard error are determined. Thus, in simple regression

$$Y = b_0 + b_1 x$$

and
$$V(Y) = s^2 \left[\frac{1}{n} + \frac{(x - \bar{x})^2}{t_{11}} \right],$$

so that fiducial limits Y_L for η the expected value of Y, are given by

$$Y_L = Y \pm ts \sqrt{\left[\frac{1}{n} + \frac{(x - \bar{x})^2}{t_{11}} \right]}. \qquad (6.3)$$

Corresponding to a range of values of x, the fiducial limits for η generate a hyperbola, which may be termed the fiducial boundary for the values of η (see Figure 6.2). Any point between the two branches of the hyperbola corresponds to an acceptable value of η and its counterpart x.

Where inverse estimation is required, a value of η is given, and the corresponding value of x may be obtained from the regression equation:

$$X = (\eta - b_0)/b_1.$$

By substituting the given value of η in the equation of the fiducial boundary (6.3), we get a quadratic equation for X. This equation will give two values for X which may be termed the inverse fiducial limits for X, given η.

It will be noted that, if the regression coefficients are accurately determined, their variance makes only a negligible contribution to the standard error of estimate, and hence to the fiducial range in direct or inverse estimation. In simple regression the variance of the regression coefficient enters into the expression for the inverse fiducial range in a term

$$\frac{t^2 s^2}{b_1^2 t_{11}},$$

which Finney (1952) has denoted by g. He remarks that if g is less than 0.05, it may usually be ignored. Our object in introducing g, however, is not for purposes of approximation but to simplify the expressions for fiducial limits.

In multiple regression we shall find it convenient to introduce the symbols

$$g_{hi} = \frac{t^2 s^2}{b_h b_i} t^{hi}. \qquad (6.4)$$

The matrix of which g_{hi} is a typical element will be denoted by G. Although it is readily derived from the inverse matrix T^{-1}, it is nevertheless convenient for expressing many of the formulas that arise in inverse estimation.

In the present instance the inverse fiducial limits are

$$X_L = \bar{x} + \frac{b_1(\eta - \bar{y}) \pm ts\sqrt{\left[\dfrac{b_1{}^2}{n} + \dfrac{(\eta - \bar{y})^2}{t_{11}} - \dfrac{t^2s^2}{nt_{11}}\right]}}{b_1{}^2 - t^2s^2/t_{11}}$$

$$= X + \frac{(X - \bar{x})\dfrac{t^2s^2}{t_{11}} \pm ts\sqrt{\left[\dfrac{b_1{}^2}{n} + \dfrac{b_1{}^2(X - \bar{x})^2}{t_{11}} - \dfrac{t^2s^2}{nt_{11}}\right]}}{b_1{}^2 - t^2s^2/t_{11}}$$

$$= X + \frac{(X - \bar{x})g \pm \dfrac{ts}{b_1}\sqrt{\left[\dfrac{(X - \bar{x})^2}{t_{11}} + \dfrac{1}{n}(1 - g)\right]}}{1 - g}.$$

Usually these limits will be real and will lie on either side of the estimate from the regression equation. But sometimes, as reference to Figure 6.2 shows, the limits may be (i) both on the same side of the estimate or (ii) nonexistent. The reason for these effects has already been discussed in Section 6.2.

Some consideration of the properties of the hyperbola is instructive. First of all, it is seen that the asymptotes are lines with slopes equidistant on either side of the slope of the regression line. The slopes of these lines represent the fiducial limits for the regression coefficient b_1. When the standard error of b_1 is so small as to be negligible within the range of application of the equation, the asymptotes converge on the regression line, and the fiducial boundaries become indistinguishable from a pair of straight lines equidistant on either side of the regression line.

When the standard error of the regression coefficient is large, the fiducial boundaries show appreciable curvature; when the regression coefficient is not significant at the chosen level, the asymptotes have slopes of opposite sign, so that one branch of the hyperbola will be cut in two places by some lines parallel to the X-axis. Naturally, we would not usually base fiducial limits on a nonsignificant regression coefficient, unless we had prior reason for assuming that a regression existed. However, sometimes the regression will be significant at one level (say 5 per cent) but not at a higher level (say 1 per cent); 95 per cent fiducial boundaries would be satisfactory, but 99 per cent boundaries would show some peculiarities.

Reference to the figure will make these results clear. It is seen that inverse limits can both lie on the same side of the estimate only when the regression coefficient is not significant. The interpretation of the result is that, corresponding to a given value of η, all values of X are acceptable

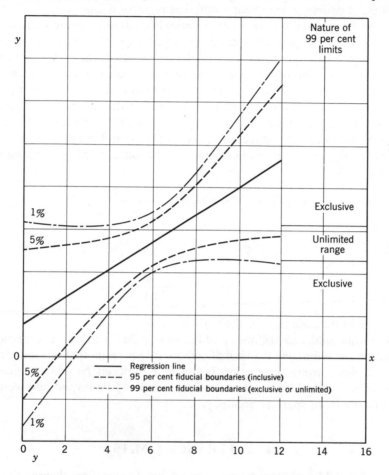

Figure 6.2.   Linear regression of y on x and fiducial boundaries.

except those in the interval shown.   On the side of the interval away from the estimate, the changed sign of the fiducial limit for β_1 has its effect, in reducing the significance of the departure.

The limits can likewise be apparently complex (actually nonexistent) only where the regression coefficient is not significant. This means that, corresponding to the given value of η any value of X is acceptable.

Needless to say, where the regression coefficient is not significant, in practice it would not be used for setting limits on X.

It will be seen that if direct fiducial limits can justifiably be calculated, inverse fiducial limits are not as satisfactory; they are somewhat wider, besides, of course, being about a different regression line.

When both variables are random variables, either regression equation may be calculated, but the appropriate equation is the regression of the predictand on the predictor. As might be expected, the direct estimate from the regression equation is more accurate than the inverse estimate from the alternative equation; this is a direct consequence of the theory of least squares. However, an alternative demonstration may be helpful. For instance, even when $Y = \bar{y}$, at which point the variance and hence the fiducial limits of a direct estimate would be independent of b_1, the limits for the inverse estimate depend on the variance of b_1. We have, when $\eta = \bar{y}$,

$$b_1{}^2(X_L - \bar{x})^2 = t^2 s^2 \left[\frac{1}{n} + \frac{(X_L - \bar{x})^2}{t_{11}} \right],$$

giving
$$X_L = \bar{x} \pm \frac{ts}{\sqrt{[n(b_1{}^2 - t^2 s^2/t_{11})]}}$$

$$= \bar{x} \pm \frac{ts}{b_1 \sqrt{[n(1 - g)]}},$$

the term in g accounting for the variance in b_1.

The wider limits are the price that has to be paid for using the regression equation for estimating the variable whose role is really that of estimator. Nevertheless, inverse estimation is the best that can be done in many situations, in which to use direct estimation would be invalid and would lead to results of spurious accuracy.

6.4 TOLERANCE LIMITS

The fiducial limits for η discussed in the previous section give the limits within which the true relationship is likely to lie. Very often the experimenter is interested also in the limits within which actual values of y, corresponding to a given value of x, may lie. Such limits, which will naturally be wider than the fiducial limits, will be called tolerance limits.

Tolerance limits are especially important for inverse estimation, for here we often have given an observed value of y (not of η) and need to be able to set limits on x. Indeed, inverse fiducial limits are seldom required, because rarely is the regression value η given.

The estimated variance of a single value y' of y about the regression line is

$$s^2\left[1 + \frac{1}{n} + \frac{(x - \bar{x})^2}{t_{11}}\right].$$

Hence, just as for fiducial limits, direct tolerance limits for values of y' corresponding to a given value of x may be determined. The limits are

$$y_L = Y \pm ts\sqrt{\left[1 + \frac{1}{n} + \frac{(x - \bar{x})^2}{t_{11}}\right]}.$$

These limits will, for varying values of x, generate a tolerance boundary which is a hyperbola with the same asymptotes as the fiducial boundary. Inverse limits may also be calculated; thus, corresponding to an observed value y' of y, we have

$$X_L = X' + \frac{\dfrac{(X' - \bar{x})t^2s^2}{t_{11}} \pm ts\sqrt{\left\{b_1^2\left[1 + \dfrac{1}{n} + \dfrac{(X' - \bar{x})^2}{t_{11}}\right] - \dfrac{(n+1)t^2s^2}{nt_{11}}\right\}}}{b_1^2 - t^2s^2/t_{11}}$$

$$= X' + \frac{(X' - \bar{x})g \pm \dfrac{ts}{b_1}\sqrt{\left[\dfrac{(X' - \bar{x})^2}{t_{11}} + \dfrac{n+1}{n}(1 - g)\right]}}{1 - g} \qquad (6.5)$$

where X' is the estimate corresponding to y'.

More generally, we may have m values of y observed at some fixed but unknown value of x. The estimated variance of the mean $\bar{y}'$ about the regression line is then

$$s^2\left[\frac{1}{m} + \frac{1}{n} + \frac{(X' - \bar{x})^2}{t_{11}}\right],$$

so that the inverse tolerance limits for the value of x will be

$$X_L = X' + \frac{(X' - \bar{x})g \pm \dfrac{ts}{b_1}\sqrt{\left[\dfrac{(X' - \bar{x})^2}{t_{11}} + \left(\dfrac{1}{m} + \dfrac{1}{n}\right)(1 - g)\right]}}{1 - g}.$$

When m is large, the inverse tolerance limits will approach the inverse fiducial limits discussed in Section 6.3.

It should be mentioned that, strictly speaking, the "inverse tolerance limits" discussed here are really not tolerance limits at all but fiducial limits, since x may be a fixed variable. However, it is convenient to retain the term "inverse tolerance limits," as a reminder of the fact that the limits are based on the tolerance boundary for the regression line and not on the fiducial boundary.

Example 6.1   Inverse Estimation of Sodium Concentration from Flame Photometer Reading. As an application of the formulas given here we may consider the estimation of sodium concentration by means of the scale reading on a flame photometer.   The data are presented and the analysis is carried out in Table 2.1.

The regression equation there given is

$$Y = -0.89 + 0.416x,$$

where x is the sodium concentration and y the photometer reading.   To be used for estimating x, the equation becomes

$$X = 2.14 + 2.404y.$$

Usually the sodium concentration will be estimated from a single reading of the photometer, so that inverse tolerance limits, given by equation (6.8), are required.

For this example, to find the 99 per cent tolerance limits, we have

$$t = 3.499$$
$$s = 0.948$$
$$b = 0.416$$
$$t_{11} = 37,500,$$

whence
$$g = 0.0017.$$

Corresponding to $y = 80$, the estimate of x is 194.4, and the inverse tolerance limits are

$$194.4 + \frac{69.4 \times 0.0017 \pm (3.499/0.416) \times 0.948 \sqrt{(0.13 + 1.11)}}{0.9983}$$

$$= 185.6 \text{ and } 203.4.$$

In this example the asymmetry introduced by g is small, and no great error would result from its neglect.

For a regression line passing through the origin the fiducial limits are a pair of lines also passing through the origin.   Thus, in Example 2.1, the line fitted through the origin is

$$Y = 0.4104x;$$

the fiducial limits for the regression coefficient are

$$0.4025 \text{ and } 0.4183,$$

so that the fiducial boundary is the pair of straight lines

$$Y = 0.4025x$$

and
$$Y = 0.4183x.$$

The inverse tolerance limits are given by

$$X_L = \frac{X \pm \dfrac{ts}{b_1'} \sqrt{\left(1 + \dfrac{X^2}{t_{11}'} - g'\right)}}{1 - g'}$$

where t_{11}' is the uncorrected sum of squares of x, and

$$g' = \frac{t^2 s^2}{b_1'^2 t_{11}'}.$$

In the example, since

$$t_{11}' = 178{,}125,$$

g' is negligible, and the inverse tolerance limits are simply

$$X_L = X \pm \frac{ts}{b_1'}\sqrt{\left(1 + \frac{X^2}{t_{11}'}\right)} \cdot$$

Thus, for $y = 80$, the estimate of x is 194.9 and the inverse tolerance limits are found to be

$$194.9 \pm \frac{3.499 \times 0.948}{0.4104}\sqrt{1.213}$$

$$= 186.0 \text{ and } 203.8.$$

We note that, although the values of the limits are altered slightly, the range differs little from that based on the regression not restricted to passing through the origin. This is so because the point considered is distant from the fixed point, the origin.

6.5   EXTENSION TO MULTIPLE REGRESSION

The methods shown above for the determination of fiducial and tolerance limits in simple regression are easily applied to multiple regression problems. With the usual notation, the regression equation is

$$Y = b_0 + b_1 x_1 + b_2 x_2 + \cdots + b_p x_p,$$

the variance of Y being estimated as

$$V(Y) = s^2\left[\frac{1}{n} + \sum_h \sum_i (x_h - \bar{x}_h)(x_i - \bar{x}_i)t^{hi}\right].$$

Fiducial limits for η are given by

$$Y \pm t\sqrt{V(Y)}.$$

In the same way, tolerance limits for y are given by

$$Y \pm t\sqrt{[s^2 + V(Y)]}.$$

The determination of inverse fiducial or tolerance limits introduces some new features. Usually what is required is a pair of limits for one of the independent variables, corresponding to given values of η (or y), and the given values of each of the other independent variables. In this case the method is similar to that used for simple regression. However, sometimes simultaneous limits for two or more of the independent variables may be required. For example, in some experiments on the feeding of supplements of molybdenum and sulphate to sheep to determine the effect of the supplements on the copper stored in the liver, it was required to determine what levels of each supplement corresponded to zero storage. On the assumption that the regression of copper storage y on level of supplement is linear, the relationship between molybdenum level (x_1) and sulphate level (x_2) estimated to give zero storage will also be linear; the fiducial boundary for X_1 and X_2 will again be a hyperbola. For this particular example, the relationship between X_1 and X_2 will be

$$b_0 + b_1 X_1 + b_2 X_2 = 0, \qquad \text{or } \bar{y} + b_1(X_1 - \bar{x}_1) + b_2(X_2 - \bar{x}_2) = 0.$$

The fiducial boundary for X_1 and X_2, referred to the point of means as origin, will be given by the equation

$$(\bar{y} + b_1 X_1 + b_2 X_2)^2 = t^2 s^2 \left(\frac{1}{n} + t^{11} X_1{}^2 + 2t^{12} X_1 X_2 + t^{22} X_2{}^2 \right). \quad (6.6)$$

This equation may be written

$$b_1{}^2 X_1{}^2 (1 - g_{11}) + 2 b_1 b_2 X_1 X_2 (1 - g_{12}) + b_2{}^2 X_2{}^2 (1 - g_{22})$$

$$+ 2\bar{y}(b_1 X_1 + b_2 X_2) + \bar{y}^2 - \frac{t^2 s^2}{n} = 0,$$

where the g_{hi} are the quantities defined in Section 6.3, equation (6.4). Its curve is a hyperbola with asymptotes through the point

$$\left[\frac{\bar{y}}{b_1} \left(\frac{g_{12} - g_{22}}{\Delta} \right), \quad \frac{\bar{y}}{b_2} \left(\frac{g_{12} - g_{11}}{\Delta} \right) \right],$$

with slopes

$$- \frac{b_1}{b_2} \left(\frac{1 - g_{12} \pm \sqrt{\Delta}}{1 - g_{22}} \right),$$

where $\Delta = (1 - g_{12})^2 - (1 - g_{11})(1 - g_{22})$.

Again, once the fiducial boundary (6.6) has been defined, there is no reason why simultaneous fiducial limits, corresponding to given values of any of the variables, may not be written down. Indeed, we could find simultaneous limits for η (or y) and one of the x_i, which would again generate a hyperbola; these limits would be both direct and inverse. Practical examples of such simultaneous limits are lacking.

Example 6.2 Inverse Estimation of Alkali Requirement for Pulping Wood to a Given Lignin Content. Another example where inverse fiducial limits are required comes from pulping studies of eucalypt woods reported by Cohen and Mackney (1951). The object is to determine a treatment which produces pulp of a required lignin content. The percentage of the wood material soluble in hot water (hot-water solubles, x_1) was determined for each wood sample, which was then divided into four parts, each being pulped with varying amounts of active alkali (x_2 per cent). The same levels are repeated for each sample, so that the two independent variables, x_1 and x_2, are uncorrelated. The lignin content of the resulting pulp was measured in terms of a "permanganate number," which is known empirically to be roughly related to lignin content, and its logarithm (y) to base 10 was taken as the dependent variable. The data are shown in Table 6.1.

TABLE 6.1

VALUES OF PERCENTAGE HOT-WATER SOLUBLES (x_1), PERCENTAGE
ACTIVE ALKALI USED IN PULPING (x_2), AND LOG PERMANGANATE
NUMBER (y) FOR SPECIMENS OF EUCALYPT WOOD

x_1	x_2	y	x_1	x_2	y	x_1	x_2	y
5.97	15	1.425	6.79	15	1.498	13.19	15	1.734
	17	1.250		17	1.330		17	1.535
	19	1.170		19	1.233		19	1.326
	21	1.124		21	1.161		21	1.201
8.00	15	1.641	9.20	15	1.442	9.52	15	1.500
	17	1.418		17	1.255		17	1.281
	19	1.230		19	1.146		19	1.152
	21	1.164		21	1.093		21	1.104
8.51	15	1.655	10.00	15	1.507	9.46	15	1.610
	17	1.384		17	1.332		17	1.425
	19	1.334		19	1.220		19	1.283
	21	1.164		21	1.199		21	1.204
4.51	15	1.486	10.94	15	1.667	3.17	15	1.204
	17	1.272		17	1.458		17	1.130
	19	1.185		19	1.258		19	1.083
	21	1.124		21	1.173		21	1.004
3.15	15	1.250	6.35	15	1.391	3.53	15	1.236
	17	1.146		17	1.207		17	1.149
	19	1.086		19	1.100		19	1.061
	21	1.033		21	1.079		21	1.025

Total	15	22.246						
	17	19.572	Means			7.486	18	1.2756
	19	17.867						
	21	16.852						
Grand total		76.537						

It is appropriate in this example to determine the regression of y on x_1 and x_2. However, what is required is to determine an estimate of, and inverse fiducial limits for, the alkali requirement X_2, which will result in a given lignin content η, when the hot-water solubles figure x_1 is known.

Since in this example the independent variables are uncorrelated, the simple and the partial regression coefficients are the same. Table 6.2 shows the calculation of these regression coefficients and the sums of squares for regression.

TABLE 6.2

CALCULATION OF REGRESSION COEFFICIENTS FROM VALUES IN TABLE 6.1

	Sum of Squares	Sum of Products with y	Regression Coefficient	Regression Sum of Squares
x_1	516.315	15.5292	$+0.030\ 077 \pm 0.0034$	0.4671
x_2	300	-17.887	$-0.059\ 623 \pm 0.0044$	1.0665
				1.5336

TABLE 6.3

ANALYSIS OF VARIANCE

	D.F.	Sum of Squares	Mean Square
Regression	2	1.5336	0.766 8**
Residual	57	0.3308	0.005 804
Total	59	1.8644	

** Significant at 1 per cent level

The analysis of variance, in Table 6.3, shows that the regression effects are highly significant and that the residual variance is 0.005 804.

The regression equation is

$$Y = 2.123 + 0.0301x_1 - 0.0596x_2$$

and the 99 per cent fiducial boundary is given by the equation

$$(Y_L - 2.123 - 0.0301x_1 + 0.0596x_2)^2$$
$$= 7.102 \times 0.005\ 804 \left[\frac{1}{60} + \frac{(x_1 - 7.486)^2}{516.315} + \frac{(x_2 - 18)^2}{300} \right]$$

The lignin content required for the pulp corresponds to a "permanganate number" of 15 (i.e., $\eta = 1.176$); this value in the equation gives the relationship

$$X_2 = 15.89 + 0.504x_1,$$

so that, once the hot-water solubles percentage is given, the requirement of active alkali can be estimated.

6.6 SOME DIFFICULTIES

Sometimes the independent variable is represented as a polynomial or similar function of the expected value of the dependent variable, rather than vice versa; in such cases it is tempting to determine the regression of the independent on the dependent variable. For instance, in an experiment on the calibration of a Stormer viscometer, liquids of varying viscosity were prepared, and the time taken for 100 revolutions of the inner cylinder of the apparatus was recorded. The theoretical relationship between viscosity (x_1) and time (y) is

$$x_1 = a_1 Y - a_{-1}/Y,$$

which is not linear in Y. It is not, however, valid to determine the regression of x_1 on y, since x_1 is not a random variable. It is necessary to rewrite the equation in the form

$$Y = \frac{x_1 + \sqrt{(x_1{}^2 + 4a_1 a_{-1})}}{2a_1}$$

or
$$Y = b_1[x_1 + \sqrt{(x_1{}^2 + c)}]$$

and to fit it by means of the methods of Chapter 4. Fortunately, in the experiment considered, it was found that a_{-1} (or c) was not significant. As a satisfactory relationship could be established with $c = 0$, this value was taken, bringing the relationship back to a simple proportionality. The modified relationship is fitted to some data in Example 4.2.

Although significance tests and fiducial limits on the constants of a nonlinear relationship are only approximate, they are nevertheless valid, as far as the methods of analysis can make them so. The fitting of the inverse relationship on the grounds that it is computationally convenient will, however, give misleading results.

6.7 ESTIMATION FROM NONLINEAR EQUATIONS

We have already seen in Chapter 4 how equations that are not linear in their parameters may be fitted and that a computational method can be devised which is effectively equivalent to the fitting of a linear regression on the nonlinear function and its first derivative with respect to the nonlinear parameter. Although it must be borne in mind that all standard errors and significance tests in this work are approximate, nevertheless, satisfactory results may be obtained by following the procedure outlined in Chapter 4.

The regression equation we consider is

$$Y = b_0 + b_1 f(x, c),$$

where b_0, b_1, and c are coefficients estimated from the data. The variance of Y may be found approximately by taking differentials, squaring, and taking expectations:

$$dY = db_0 + f\,db_1 + b_1 f' dc$$
$$= db_0 + f\,db_1 + f' db_2,$$

where we put $b_1 dc = db_2$, after the manner of Chapter 4. From this point the variance of estimate is found in exactly the same way as from linear equations. We find, for the estimated variance,

$$V(Y) = s^2 \left[\frac{1}{n} + (f - \bar{f})^2 t^{11} + 2(f - \bar{f})(f' - \bar{f'})t^{12} + (f' - \bar{f'})^2 t^{22} \right].$$

Since the quantities t^{hi} and s^2 have already been calculated for the determination of the regression equation, the variance calculation is no more troublesome than it would be had the equations been linear.

Example 6.3   Variance of Estimated Change in Total Liver Copper (Example 4.1). Suppose that the estimated change in total liver copper, corresponding to a daily molybdenum intake of 10 mg., is required.

From the equation we have

$$Y_{10} = -4.85 + 65.3 e^{-1.66}$$
$$= -4.85 + 65.3 \times 0.1902$$
$$= 7.6$$
$$f - \bar{f} = 0.1902 - 0.3627 = -0.1725$$
$$f' - \bar{f'} = -1.902 + 0.745 = -1.157$$
$$V(Y_{10}) = 46.20\,(\tfrac{1}{6} + 0.1725^2 \times 1.2505 + 2 \times 0.1725 \times 1.157 \times 0.19311$$
$$+ 1.157^2 \times 0.316\,889)$$
$$= 32.58$$
$$\text{S.E.}(Y_{10}) = 5.7.$$

6.8 SEPARATING OUT EFFECTS BY REGRESSION ANALYSIS

In many of the practical applications of regression analysis, the value of the technique lies not so much in enabling one variable to be predicted from another as in assessing the magnitude of the effects of one or more factors, and in separating out the contributions of each factor. In such applications the regression coefficients are of interest in themselves, and not merely for providing the coefficients in an equation of prediction. For example, in an industrial process, it may not be possible to determine directly the effects of certain process variables on the quality of the finished product.   However, if factory records provide values of each of these process variables from time to time and also the corresponding values of the product quality, regression analysis may be used to derive estimates of the effect of each variable.

6.9   THE "DAILY TOTAL" METHOD

In studying costs in logging and sawmilling in the timber industry, it has been found too laborious to record times and other information for individual logs.   Even when this has been done, the problem of allocating lost time, time for repairs, and other costs has not been satisfactorily solved.   An alternative method of determining costs has been to record the daily totals of each item and to determine the relation between cost and other factors as a regression equation.   For example, Hasel (1946) has in this way derived an estimate for logging cost in terms of tree size and intensity of cutting.   For his records he has used not observations on individual trees but total daily cost and daily totals of numbers of logs in each size class, quantities that would normally be recorded in any case. He is thus able to derive information on costs without the labor of collecting individual records.   Schumacher and Jones (1940) and Littler and Adkins (1954) have applied this "daily total" method of determining the relation between milling cost and dimensions of logs in studies of sawmill economics.

The daily total method simplifies the work of the mill study because records can be kept without interfering with the operation of the mill (by time keeping, etc.).   The total cost may be reckoned as proportional to total time worked;   total output only, and not output from individual trees or logs, need be recorded.   Indeed, the daily total method may be considered to give a more realistic picture of mill or logging operation than a detailed study of individual logs.   If it is less accurate because it records fewer details, it also requires a smaller study crew, so that for a study of the same cost more mills can be studied, or more days spent at the one mill.

An interesting application of a method the same in principle as the daily total method is given by Day (1937).   She has derived equations for estimating the cost of hauling logs, in terms of the diameter and diameter squared.   Seventy truckloads of logs, for each of which the haulage cost was the same, were examined.   For each, the number of logs and the totals of diameters and diameters squared were recorded.   A relation giving cost was determined by regression analysis.   The success of the method is indicated by the fact that, using the empirical formula, the haulage cost of any truckload was estimated with a standard error of 10 per cent.

Needless to say, the applications of this and similar methods are not confined to forestry operations and should have wide usefulness in factory operations and costing.

6.10   ESTIMATION OF ZEROS, ETC., OF A FITTED CURVE

Having fitted a polynomial regression, we are often interested in determining the value of the independent variable for which the estimate of the dependent variable vanishes, that is, in finding the zeros of Y. It is just as easy to find the values of x for which Y takes any other given value, say a, for we then seek simply the zeros of $Y - a$.

This problem is one of inverse estimation: given a value of the dependent variable, to find the corresponding values of the independent variables. It differs from inverse estimation in multiple regression, however, in that the required values of the independent variable are a set of points rather than a single point, line, or plane, etc.

If the regression equation is

$$Y = b_0 + b_1 x + b_2 x^2 + \cdots + b_p x^p,$$

the zeros are the roots of the equation

$$b_0 + b_1 x + b_2 x^2 + \cdots + b_p x^p = 0. \tag{6.7}$$

This equation will have p roots in general, but an even number of them may be complex. From a practical point of view, the complex roots are of no interest. It may happen, though, that the roots found complex in the sample correspond to real roots in the population; that is, they are complex as a result of sampling errors in the coefficients of the equation (6.7). Hence it is of interest to determine fiducial limits for the zeros of the equation. If the fiducial limits found are real, even when the root itself is complex, there is evidence for the existence of a couple of real roots. This will be clear from inspection of Figure 6.3, which gives a parabola and its fiducial boundaries, placed in varying relationship to the X-axis. In (i) we see a curve with real zeros, each of which has real fiducial limits. In (ii), the curve has real zeros, but one pair of fiducial limits is complex; in practice this means that the inner limits coalesce, and there is also the possibility that the zero does not exist (i.e., the population roots are not real). In (iii), the curve has no real zeros, but a pair of fiducial limits exists, indicating the possibility of real zeros in the population. In elucidating such a problem, a diagram such as that given is often more satisfactory than a purely algebraic discussion.

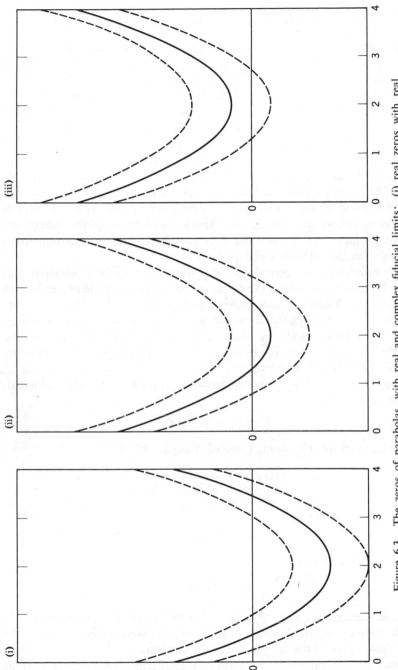

Figure 6.3. The zeros of parabolas, with real and complex fiducial limits: (i) real zeros with real limits, (ii) real zeros with one pair of complex limits, (iii) complex zeros with one pair of real limits.

6.11 MAXIMA, ETC., OF A FITTED CURVE

Sometimes a parabolic or other polynomial curve is fitted to data with the object of determining the maximum or minimum value taken by the dependent variable and the value of the independent variable for which it occurs. A detailed account of the determination of maxima is given by Hotelling (1941), whose paper is a model of investigation. Hotelling discusses the question of allocation of experimental points for most accurate estimation of maxima; this is beyond the scope of this book, for we consider only the estimation of the maximum from a regression equation of given form, determined from a given set of experimental points. Hotelling's work is concerned solely with the efficient use of the regression relation to determine a maximum. Very often the object of the experimenter is not so specialized; the position and value of the maximum, although important, are not the only useful items of information to be drawn from the regression equation.

For example, in an agricultural experiment it may be considered that there is an optimum level of fertilizer giving maximum yield of a crop, and that levels of fertilizer above the optimum give reduced yields. A simple way of testing this supposition would be to fit a parabola to the relation of yield to fertilizer level. A significant negative quadratic term in the parabola would indicate the existence of a maximum yield corresponding to the optimum fertilizer level.

The optimum value of the independent variable is readily estimated. If the equation is

$$Y = b_0 + b_1 x + b_2 x^2,$$

the maximum (or minimum) value of Y occurs when

$$\frac{dY}{dx} = b_1 + 2b_2 x = 0,$$

so that the estimate is

$$x_m = -b_1/2b_2,$$

the value of Y then being

$$b_0 - b_1^2/4b_2.$$

This is a maximum if b_2 is negative, a minimum if b_2 is positive. In what follows we shall always speak of maxima, although the same principles apply to the determination of minima.

Since x_m is a ratio of two regression coefficients, its variance may be found approximately in terms of the variances of b_1 and b_2. We have, approximately,

$$V(x_m) = s^2\left(\frac{t^{11}}{4b_2{}^2} - \frac{b_1 t^{12}}{2b_2{}^3} + \frac{b_1{}^2 t^{22}}{4b_2{}^4}\right).$$

Using this variance, we may calculate approximate fiducial limits for the value of the optimum. These limits are

$$X_L = x_m[1 \pm \sqrt{(g_{11} - 2g_{12} + g_{22})}].$$

Alternatively, we may determine exact fiducial limits by the method given in Section 6.2 for the fiducial limits of a ratio. The fiducial limits are the roots of the equation

$$(2b_2 X + b_1)^2 = t^2 s^2 (4t^{22} X^2 + 4t^{12} X + t^{11}),$$

which may be written

$$(X - x_m)^2 = g_{22} X^2 - 2g_{12} x_m X + g_{11} x_m{}^2$$

and has the solutions

$$X_L = x_m\left\{\frac{1 - g_{12} \pm \sqrt{[(1 - g_{12})^2 - (1 - g_{11})(1 - g_{22})]}}{1 - g_{22}}\right\}.$$

For the maximum value of Y, which we write Y_m, we can determine only an approximate variance, and hence approximate fiducial limits. We have

$$Y_m = b_0 - b_1{}^2/4b_2$$
$$= \bar{y} - b_1 \bar{x}_1 - b_2 \bar{x}_2 - b_1{}^2/4b_2,$$

where $\quad \bar{x}_2 = Sx^2/n.$

Hence, taking differentials,

$$dY_m = d\bar{y} - (\bar{x}_1 + b_1/2b_2)\,db_1 - (\bar{x}_2 - b_1{}^2/4b_2{}^2)\,db_2$$
$$= d\bar{y} - (\bar{x}_1 - x_m)\,db_1 - (\bar{x}_2 - x_m{}^2)\,db_2.$$

On squaring both sides and taking expectations, we find the approximate variance, whose estimate from the sample is

$$V(Y_m) = s^2\left[\frac{1}{n} + (\bar{x}_1 - x_m)^2 t^{11} + 2(\bar{x}_1 - x_m)(\bar{x}_2 - x_m{}^2)t^{12}\right.$$
$$\left. + (\bar{x}_2 - x_m{}^2)^2 t^{22}\right]. \quad (6.8)$$

As explained in Section 6.2, the fact that the fiducial limits for the value of x_m include infinity (or, as it is sometimes expressed, the limits are exclusive) indicates that there is no evidence for the existence of a maximum; in other words, the coefficient b_2 is not significant at the level of significance chosen.

6.12   EXAMPLE OF ESTIMATING A MAXIMUM

Example 6.4   The pH of Ret Liquor at Which the Rate of Retting is Maximized. One method of retting flax is to steep it in water for several days, so that bacteria selectively attack the straw, removing the material binding the fiber bundles together. The rate at which the retting takes place is measured by the change in buffer capacity of the ret liquor; it is found that the rate increases with increasing pH of ret liquor and then falls off as pH increases still further.

The data analyzed to determine the maximum rate came from an experiment in which flax at various stages of maturity was retted, there being in all fourteen rets; the pH and buffer capacity rate (among other things) were measured at five times during the ret. Although the observations at different times may not be independent, the data are nevertheless satisfactory for determining the maximum; the disturbance to the fiducial limits is not likely to be serious. The quadratic regression of rate (y) on pH (x) was determined from the sums of squares and products for the interaction of rets and times, with 52 degrees of freedom. The relevant sums of squares and products are set out in Table 6.4, the inverse matrix and the regression coefficients with their standard errors in Table 6.5. The analysis of variance, the purpose of which is to provide the residual mean square from which to estimate the standard errors of the regression coefficients, is given in Table 6.6.

TABLE 6.4

SUMS OF SQUARES AND PRODUCTS FOR DETERMINING QUADRATIC REGRESSION OF BUFFER CAPACITY RATE (y) ON pH (x)

$$
\begin{array}{ccc}
x & x^2 & y \\
\begin{bmatrix} 0.6802 & 6.5126 \\ 6.5126 & 62.3770 \end{bmatrix} & & \begin{array}{c} -0.094\ 56 \\ -0.921\ 14 \\ 0.077\ 998 \end{array}
\end{array}
$$

TABLE 6.5

INVERSE MATRIX AND REGRESSION COEFFICIENTS

$$
\begin{bmatrix} 4192.950 & -437.773\ 6 \\ -437.7736 & 45.722\ 69 \end{bmatrix} \quad
\begin{array}{c} b_i \\ 6.765\ 42 \pm 2.1 \\ -0.721\ 127 \pm 0.22 \end{array}
$$

TABLE 6.6

ANALYSIS OF VARIANCE OF BUFFER CAPACITY RATE

	D.F.	Sum of Squares	Mean Square
Regression	2	0.024 521	0.012 260
Residual	50	0.053 477	0.001 070
Total	52	0.077 998	

Since the quadratic regression is significant at the 1 per cent level, it is appropriate to calculate the position of the maximum rate and its 99 per cent fiducial limits.   We have

$$x_m = -b_1/2b_2 = 6.765/(2 \times 0.7211)$$
$$= 4.69.$$

The fiducial limits are found as follows:
For 50 degrees of freedom,
$$F = 7.171$$
so that $$Fs^2 = 0.007\ 669.$$

From this and the matrix T^{-1} and the regression coefficients given in Table 6.5 we derive the matrix G (Table 6.7).   The fiducial limits are, then,

$$4.69\left[\frac{0.3118 \pm \sqrt{(0.3118^2 - 0.2974 \times 0.3257)}}{0.3257}\right]$$

$$= 4.69 \times \frac{0.899}{1.015}$$

$$= 4.22 \text{ and } 4.76.$$

TABLE 6.7
THE MATRIX G

$$\begin{bmatrix} 0.7026 & 0.6882 \\ 0.6882 & 0.6743 \end{bmatrix}$$

From the values of the g_{hi} it is clear that the approximate fiducial limits will be inaccurate.   The approximate limits are, in fact,

$$4.58 \text{ and } 4.80,$$

which are clearly unsatisfactory.

In this example the actual maximum rate will vary from ret to ret and is not of interest.   However, were its standard error required, this would be given approximately by formula (6.8), with n put equal to 5 and $\bar{x}_1$ and $\bar{x}_2$ taking the values of the mean for the ret considered.

6.13   EXTENSION TO HIGHER DERIVATIVES

An interesting example of how these ideas may be extended arises in experiments on the retting of flax similar to that discussed in Example 6.4. The buffer capacity of the retting liquor is taken as a measure of the stage the ret has reached;   the rate of change of buffer capacity is accordingly considered to measure the rate of retting.   In studying the progress of the ret, it is of interest to know when the retting rate reaches its maximum. Rather than the buffer capacity *rate*, we may take the buffer capacity itself as the dependent variable and determine its regression on time.   If this may be represented by a polynomial, the time of the maximum rate of retting may be found as the time when the second derivative of this polynomial vanishes. Thus, if the equation is

$$Y = b_0 + b_1 x + b_2 x^2 + b_3 x^3$$

where x is the time and y the buffer capacity, then

$$d^2 Y/dx^2 = 2b_2 + 6b_3 x.$$

The time of maximum rate of retting is therefore

$$x_m = -b_2/3b_3.$$

The treatment of this problem, including the determination of fiducial limits for x_m and the maximum rate, follows exactly the same lines as that of estimating a maximum.

6.14 MAXIMA OF POLYNOMIAL CURVES

The maxima of polynomial curves in general may be estimated in the same way as the maximum of a parabola, but since there is in general more than one maximum (or minimum), and because the equation for the maximum may yield complex roots, the general case needs separate discussion.

The principles are made sufficiently clear from the discussion of an equation of the fourth degree. Suppose that the regression equation is

$$Y = b_0 + b_1 x + b_2 x^2 + b_3 x^3 + b_4 x^4.$$

Then the equation for the position of the maximum is

$$b_1 + 2b_2 x + 3b_3 x^2 + 4b_4 x^3 = 0. \tag{6.9}$$

This equation has certainly one real root, the other two roots being either both real or both complex.

Since a curve of the fourth degree may have two maxima and one minimum (or two minima and one maximum), the most direct way of finding out the required maximum is to plot the curve or prepare a table of Y for various values of x. Equation (6.9) has value in giving the maximum accurately. Also, if fiducial limits for the position of the maximum are required, recourse must be had to algebraic methods. The fiducial limits are a set of six values, two for each of the three roots of (6.9), given by the sixth-degree equation

$$(b_1 + 2b_2 x + 3b_3 x^2 + 4b_4 x^3)^2 = t^2 s^2 [t^{11} + 4t^{12} x + (4t^{22} + 6t^{13}) x^2$$
$$+ (12t^{23} + 8t^{14}) x^3 + (9t^{33} + 16t^{24}) x^4$$
$$+ 24t^{34} x^5 + 16t^{44} x^6].$$

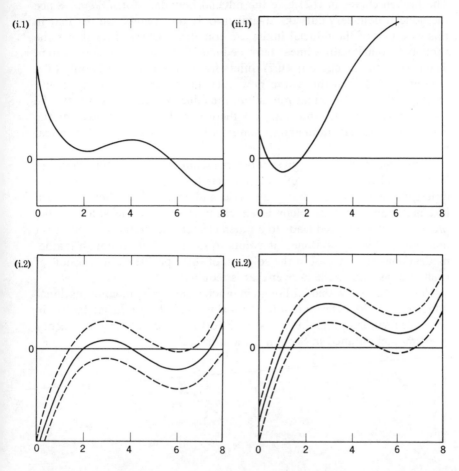

Figure 6.4.   Fitted curves and curves of their derivatives, showing maxima and minima and their fiducial limits: (i) one maximum and two minima, with four real and two complex limits, (ii) one minimum but four real limits.

In discussing the parabolic case, we pointed out that the fiducial limits determined from such an equation could be complex, even though the position of the maximum is necessarily real.   For higher-degree polynomials it is, on the other hand, also possible for the position of some of the maxima to be complex, although fiducial limits for them are real.   This point may be made clear by examining the diagrams of Figure 6.4.   The curves show Y and dY/dx plotted against x, for various polynomials Y. Curve (i.1) shows a polynomial with one maximum and two minima, whose positions are given by the points where curve (i.2) cuts the X-axis.

The broken curves in (i.2) give the fiducial boundary for dY/dx. Since the fiducial boundary cuts the X-axis in only four points, we see that in this case two of the fiducial limits are complex. Curve (ii.1) shows the same polynomial with a linear term deducted. It has but one minimum. The corresponding curve in (ii.2) differs from the curve in (i.2) only by a constant. Although this curve now cuts the X-axis in only one point, corresponding to the extant minimum, the fiducial boundaries still cut the X-axis in four points, showing that there is still some evidence for the existence of the maximum and minimum whose estimates do not take real values.

Inspection of the curves gives a better picture of the situation than can be conveyed by any description; it is left to the reader to examine the different possible cases that may arise and to consider their practical interpretation. This problem is an example of how the study of the practical issues involved leads to a much clearer interpretation than direct mathematical analysis alone; it points to the fact that, although mathematical analysis is a tool in the solution of these problems, it will not, of itself, always lead to the answer that is required.

These results show that, although in practice there may be computational difficulties in the determination of maxima and their fiducial limits, in principle their determination is a straightforward application of the theory of estimation outlined in Section 1.9 and in Section 6.2.

CHAPTER 7

The Analysis of Covariance

7.1 ANALOGY OF COVARIANCE ANALYSIS AND MULTIPLE REGRESSION

When an experiment is carried out to study the effects of different factors on a variable, it is desirable to keep the values of all extraneous factors under control as far as possible. Some factors cannot be controlled, however, or it may be impracticable to try to do so; but if their values can be measured, this additional information may be used to improve the accuracy of the results for the variable studied. For example, in determining the effect of rate of loading on the modulus of rupture of timber specimens, it is not always possible to control temperature and humidity. If these variables are measured at the time of test, it is possible to make an adjustment for their effects. In many cases it is found sufficiently accurate to make an empirical linear adjustment, based on prior knowledge, to correct the results to a chosen temperature and humidity. If the correction factor for the variable x is c, the corrected value of the dependent variable y will be

$$y - c(x - \bar{x}).$$

When c is an empirical adjustment, the corrected values may be analyzed in the same way as the original values would have been. In other cases, where there is no prior knowledge, the effect of the extraneous variables may be eliminated by means of a regression adjustment.

One incidental advantage of employing a regression adjustment for extraneous variables is that it enables the magnitude of their effects to be estimated and tested for significance. It will often be worthwhile to make a regression adjustment, even when the regression is not significant; but a significance test, taken in conjunction with other information, will enable the experimenter to decide which variables are worth adjusting for.

It can be seen that the regression method of adjustment for extraneous variables is equivalent, formally, to the determination of a multiple regression including both the treatments and the extraneous variables.

117

The adjustment of the effects of the treatments is analogous to the change from a simple to a partial regression coefficient. Indeed, in multiple regression the same result is obtained by adjusting the dependent and all the controlled variables for the uncontrolled variables, as would be obtained from a regression on all variables, controlled and uncontrolled. Thus, the methods of adjustment given here could quite logically have been discussed in Chapter 3.[1] However, when the treatments are categories rather than numerical variables, it is for practical and computational reasons more convenient to discuss their adjustment in terms of the analysis of covariance than in terms of multiple regression. But before proceeding to do this, we need to consider further the role that the independent variables may play in the analysis. The reader may at each point satisfy himself of the analogy with multiple regression.

7.2 ENVIRONMENTAL AND EXPLANATORY VARIABLES

In regression analysis an independent variable may be included for one of two reasons: (i) as an estimator of the dependent variable, accounting to a considerable extent for the variation in the latter; and (ii) as a correction to the dependent and the other independent variables, so strengthening the relationship found between them. In covariance analysis the distinction is an important one; although the mechanism of the analysis is the same for both types of variables, the interpretation is different. When, as in the example just given, the concomitant variables, temperature and humidity, are unaffected by treatment, but are correlated with the dependent variable, so that they may be used to reduce its error, we shall call them *environmental* variables, since they represent uncontrolled environmental effects. In other cases the concomitants may be affected by the treatments also, and then the question arises whether the effect of treatment on the variable being studied may be explained in terms of its effect on the concomitants. The adjustment for the concomitants is really a means of eliminating from the dependent variable the part of the treatment effect that is attributable to the effect of the treatments on the concomitants. Variables treated in this way will be termed *explanatory*.

Clearly, an explanatory variable may also be subject to error variation which is correlated with that of the dependent variable and is therefore environmental. Even so, its importance lies not in its reducing the error

---

[1] A factor which is tested at $p + 1$ levels leads to an analysis with p degrees of freedom for the factor. Formally, this analysis is equivalent to a regression on p independent variables. Indeed, the p independent comparisons among the variants of the factor may for many purposes be conveniently represented as p pseudovariables, suitably defined.

variance but in its affording an explanation of the treatment effects. In practice, an environmental variable is one that is independent of the treatments, for instance, a variable observed before the experiment is performed. If a presumed environmental variable is found to be significantly affected by treatments, an explanation must be sought and the effect allowed for in the interpretation of the data.

7.3   EXAMPLE OF AN ENVIRONMENTAL VARIABLE

The actual calculation and interpretation of a covariance analysis are best made clear by means of examples; the first is the adjustment for an environmental variable.

Example 7.1   The Effect of Temperature on the Maximum Compressive Strength of Specimens of Hoop Pine (Araucaria cunninghamii), Adjusted for Variations in Moisture Content. In a series of experiments (Sulzberger, 1953) on the effect of temperature on the strength properties of timber species, specimens were tested over a range of temperatures and at various moisture contents. The moisture content of 20 per cent could be maintained only in conditions of high humidity and was therefore difficult to control. For the specimens tested in this condition, therefore, the moisture content varied considerably, so a covariance adjustment for the effect of moisture content was made to these data. For each species, material from ten trees was taken, two specimens from each being tested at each temperature. The results for the maximum compressive strength parallel to the grain for hoop pine are set out in Table 7.1.

The first step in the analysis is to compute the sums of squares and products of the two variables, attributable to the different factors. The total variation is split up into parts corresponding to trees and temperatures, leaving a residual attributable to experimental error. This leads to an analysis such as is set out in the first five columns of Table 7.2. The calculations are described in standard textbooks dealing with the analysis of variance. The sums of squares between temperatures, for instance, are derived from the totals for each temperature, that for y being

$$\frac{151,350^2 + 135,450^2 + 105,050^2 + 84,190^2 + 65,170^2}{20} - \frac{541,210^2}{100}$$

$$= 252,123,000.$$

The other sums of squares and products are calculated in a similar manner.

The "residual" line of Table 7.2 gives sums of squares and products from which the effects of temperature and of variation between trees have been eliminated. The regression coefficient of maximum compressive strength on moisture content is calculated from these sums of squares and products:

$$b = -6323.1/35.1846$$
$$= -179.7.$$

TABLE 7.1

MAXIMUM COMPRESSIVE STRENGTH PARALLEL TO GRAIN (y) AND
MOISTURE CONTENT (x, NOMINALLY 20 PER CENT) OF HOOP PINE
SPECIMENS, AT DIFFERENT TEMPERATURES

Totals of Pairs from Same Tree

Tree	Temperature, °C.										Total	
	−20		0		20		40		60			
	y	x	y	x	y	x	y	x	y	x	y	x
1	13,140	42.1	12,460	41.1	9,430	43.1	7,630	41.4	6,340	39.1	49,000	206.8
2	15,900	41.0	14,110	39.4	11,300	40.3	9,560	38.6	7,270	36.7	58,140	196.0
3	13,390	41.1	12,320	40.2	9,650	40.6	7,900	41.7	6,410	39.7	49,670	203.3
4	15,510	40.1	13,680	39.8	10,330	40.4	8,270	39.8	7,060	39.3	54,850	199.4
5	15,530	41.0	13,160	41.2	10,290	39.7	8,670	39.0	6,680	39.0	54,330	199.9
6	15,260	42.0	13,640	40.0	10,350	40.3	8,670	40.9	6,620	41.2	54,540	204.4
7	15,060	40.4	13,250	39.0	10,560	34.9	8,100	40.1	6,150	41.4	53,120	195.8
8	15,210	39.3	13,540	38.8	10,460	37.5	8,300	40.6	6,090	41.8	53,600	198.0
9	16,900	39.2	15,230	38.5	11,940	38.5	9,340	39.4	6,260	41.7	59,670	197.3
10	15,450	37.7	14,060	35.7	10,740	36.7	7,750	38.9	6,290	38.2	54,290	187.2
Total	151,350	403.9	135,450	393.7	105,050	392.0	84,190	400.4	65,170	398.1	541,210	1,988.1

This coefficient is the appropriate correction to be applied to adjust for random variations in moisture content. The mean values of maximum compressive strength and moisture content for each temperature, and the means for the former corrected to 20 per cent moisture content, are set out in Table 7.3.

The covariance adjustment for the independent variable may be applied to the treatment means even when its effect is not significant, just as effects of variation between trees or those caused by other external factors would be eliminated whether or not they were significant. However, the improvement due to covariance is not likely to be large unless the regression is significant. The analysis of the residual variation in Table 7.4 shows that the regression is in this case highly significant.

TABLE 7.2

ANALYSIS OF COVARIANCE OF MAXIMUM COMPRESSIVE STRENGTH (y)
AND MOISTURE CONTENT (x)

| | | Sums of Squares and Products | | | y, Adjusted for x | | |
	D.F.	y^2	xy	x^2	D.F.	S.S.	M.S.
Trees	9	9,503,300	−7,610.1	27.1469			
Temperatures							
Linear	1	250,029,500	5,478.7	0.1200			
Deviation	3	2,093,500	−755.5	4.5974	3	1,970,300	656,800**
Total	4	252,123,000	4,723.2	4.7174			
Residual	36	4,187,400	−6,323.1	35.1846	35	3,051,100	87,170
Total	49	265,813,700	−9,210.0	67.0489			

** Significant at 1 per cent level

TABLE 7.3

ORIGINAL AND CORRECTED MEANS OF MAXIMUM COMPRESSIVE
STRENGTH

Temperature, °C.	y	x	$y - b(x - 20)$
−20	7568	20.20	7603
0	6772	19.68	6716
20	5252	19.60	5181
40	4210	20.02	4213
60	3258	19.90	3241

TABLE 7.4

TEST OF RESIDUAL REGRESSION OF MAXIMUM COMPRESSIVE
STRENGTH ON MOISTURE CONTENT

	D.F.	Sum of Squares	Mean Square
Regression	1	1,136,300	1,136,300**
Residual, reduced	35	3,051,100	87,170
Residual	36	4,187,400	116,320

** Significant at 1 per cent level

The regression sum of squares is determined as

$$(-6323.1)^2/35.1846 = 1,136,300.$$

The residual mean square is reduced from 116,320 to 87,170, giving an increase in efficiency of about 33 per cent. This means that the use of covariance has improved the accuracy to about the same extent as increasing the number of trees from 10 to 13.

Incidentally, the analysis of variance of the moisture contents furnishes no evidence that moisture content has been affected by temperature; the relevant mean squares are

Temperatures	1.1794
Residual	0.9774.

There is therefore no reason why moisture content should not be employed as an environmental variable.

7.4   SIGNIFICANCE OF TREATMENT EFFECTS AFTER ADJUSTMENT

There remains now the question of testing the significance of the effects of temperature after the adjustment for moisture content has been made. Since in this work it was expected that the regression of compressive strength on temperature would be linear, it is first necessary to test the significance of the deviation from linearity. For this reason the sums of squares and products for temperature in Table 7.2 have been partitioned into components for linear trend and deviation from linearity.

Since a common regression coefficient has been used in correcting the means shown in Table 7.3, these means are correlated. These correlations need to be allowed for in testing the significance of treatment comparisons. Just as, in multiple regression, the adjustment of the dependent variable for one of the independent variables affects the relations between it and the remaining independent variables, so in covariance analysis the adjustment affects not only the residual sum of squares but also the sums of squares for treatment comparisons. Treatment comparisons here take the role of the remaining independent variables.

However, the significance of these comparisons may be tested by a simple device. Suppose that we wish to test the significance of deviation of the corrected means from a linear relation with temperature. The null hypothesis implies that the sum of squares for deviation from linearity and the residual sum of squares are homogeneous apart from any effects of moisture content. Accordingly, these two lines of the analysis may be pooled, and a correction derived, based on the pooled sums of squares and products. The analysis is shown in Table 7.5. Here the sum of squares for regression is

$$(-7078.6)^2/39.7820 = 1,259,500.$$

The reduced pooled sum of squares, with 38 degrees of freedom, is by hypothesis comparable with the reduced residual sum of squares from Table 7.4, which it includes. The difference between these two represents deviation from linearity, adjusted for the effects of moisture content.

TABLE 7.5

TEST OF DEVIATION FROM LINEARITY, ADJUSTED FOR MOISTURE
CONTENT

	D.F.	Sums of Squares and Products			Mean Square
		y^2	xy	x^2	
Deviation plus residual	39	6,280,900	−7,078.6	39.7820	
Regression	1	1,259,500			
Deviation plus residual, reduced	38	5,021,400			
Residual, reduced	35	3,051,100			87,170
Deviation, adjusted	3	1,970,300			656,800**

** Significant at 1 per cent level

The analysis shows that deviation from linearity is still highly significant, although the sum of squares is reduced from 2,093,500 to 1,970,300 by the adjustment. The most direct way of calculating the adjusted sum of squares is to add to the original sum of squares for deviations the residual regression sum of squares and deduct the pooled regression sum of squares; thus,

$$2{,}093{,}500 + 1{,}136{,}300 - 1{,}259{,}500 = 1{,}970{,}300.$$

The analysis of adjusted values is presented in the final three columns of Table 7.2.

Since the adjustment to the sum of squares for deviation consists of the difference of two regression sums of squares, it may be either positive or negative. For this reason, although we speak of a reduced sum of squares when the associated degrees of freedom are reduced by the number of covariance variables eliminated, we speak of an adjusted sum of squares when the degrees of freedom are unaltered.

A further analysis of the treatment comparisons is often of interest. Considering still the deviation from linearity, we may derive a reduced sum of squares, with two degrees of freedom, from a regression based on the deviation line of Table 7.2. The difference between the adjusted and the reduced sums of squares is a sum of squares representing the difference of regressions from the deviation and the residual lines of the analysis; this difference of regressions may also be interpreted as the regression of the temperatures component of y on x (Williams, 1954). In some situations, although not in the present one, it is of interest to examine separately the magnitude of these two effects. The analysis of Table 7.6 confirms what

TABLE 7.6

PARTITION OF THE ADJUSTED SUM OF SQUARES FOR DEVIATIONS

	D.F.	Sum of Squares	Mean Square
Difference of regressions	1	900	$900^{(n)}$
Deviation, reduced	2	1,969,400	984,700**
Deviation, adjusted	3	1,970,300	

$^{(n)}$ Not significant
** Significant at 1 per cent level

might have been judged from Table 7.2, that the regression coefficients from the deviation and residual lines (-164.3 and -179.7 respectively) do not differ significantly.

7.5 STANDARD ERRORS OF ADJUSTED MEANS

As shown in the preceding section, the significance of any comparison among the adjusted means may be tested by an analysis of variance. However, it is convenient to quote the standard error of the comparison. Suppose two means, y and y', of n and n' values respectively, are being compared, and that x and x' are the corresponding values of the independent variable. If b is the regression coefficient from the residual line of the analysis, the adjusted difference is

$$y - y' - b(x - x')$$

and its estimated variance

$$s^2\left[\frac{1}{n} + \frac{1}{n'} + \frac{(x - x')^2}{t_{11}}\right]; \qquad (7.1)$$

in this expression s^2 is the reduced residual variance of y and t_{11} the residual sum of squares of x. The same method is adopted in determining the variance of more complicated comparisons.

The variance of the adjusted comparison differs from that of the unadjusted in two respects: the residual variance of y is reduced by regression on x, and the factor

$$\left(\frac{1}{n} + \frac{1}{n'}\right)$$

is increased to

$$\left[\frac{1}{n} + \frac{1}{n'} + \frac{(x - x')^2}{t_{11}}\right],$$

to allow for errors in the regression coefficient. Finney (1946), noticing that the increase due to the second cause, averaged over all comparisons, was

$$\frac{m}{t_{11}},$$

where m is the treatments mean square for x, has suggested combining both these factors in one *effective* reduced residual mean square, namely

$$s^2\left(1 + \frac{m}{t_{11}}\right).$$

For many purposes it will be sufficiently accurate to use the effective variance thus defined, rather than to use a different expression such as (7.1) for each comparison.

Since the variance of each comparison is affected by the errors in the regression coefficient, it seems appropriate to base any estimate of the efficiency of the use of covariance on the effective variance. Thus, in Example 7.1, the effective reduced residual mean square is

$$87,170\left(1 + \frac{1.1794}{35.1846}\right)$$

$$= 90,090,$$

and the efficiency of the covariance analysis is more correctly estimated as

$$\frac{116,320}{90,090} = 1.29,$$

or an increase of 29 per cent.

7.6 EXAMPLE OF AN EXPLANATORY VARIABLE

Example 7.2 The Effect of Loss in Weight Due to Fungal Decay on the Impact Strength of Specimens of Coachwood (Ceratopetalum apetalum). In a study of the effects of fungal decay on the mechanical strength of timber, specimens of coachwood were exposed for varying periods to fungal decay. The specimens were weighed before and after decay and then subjected to the Izod impact test. In Table 7.7 are shown for each specimen the percentage loss in weight (x) and the corresponding Izod value (y). It was hoped that the Izod value could be satisfactorily estimated from the loss in weight. This would mean that the loss in weight would also account for the effect of duration of exposure to fungal decay on the Izod value of the specimens.

The analysis of variance and covariance is set out in Table 7.8. Inspection of the table shows that, as might be expected, the effect of treatment on weight loss is highly significant (mean squares for treatments and residual, 895.1 and 25.51 respectively; $F = 35.1$); hence weight loss is a possible explanatory variable.

TABLE 7.7

IZOD VALUES (y) AND PERCENTAGE LOSS IN WEIGHT (x) OF 42
COACHWOOD SPECIMENS AFTER EXPOSURE FOR VARYING TIMES TO
FUNGAL DECAY

26 Days		35 Days		49 Days		63 Days	
y	x	y	x	y	x	y	x
30	8.0	34	9.1	27	15.0	16	23.4
28	10.5	19	19.4	20	21.0	16	28.2
30	8.2	22	20.5	14	24.2	20	29.5
29	13.0	25	14.2	18	15.3	16	22.2
28	10.1	22	11.0	12	17.3	6	40.2
17	16.2	25	19.1	18	24.7	16	36.6
24	16.1	22	16.0	13	23.9	12	35.5
22	13.4	23	11.1	21	20.2	11	42.1
30	13.0	28	12.0	24	13.6	9	42.5
30	7.3	24	17.1			22	25.8
25	14.0	30	13.3				
		24	8.9				
293	129.8	298	171.7	167	175.2	144	326.0
No. 11		12		9		10	

TABLE 7.8

ANALYSIS OF COVARIANCE OF IZOD VALUE AND PERCENTAGE
LOSS IN WEIGHT

	D.F.	Sums of Squares and Products		
		y^2	xy	x^2
Treatments	3	1005.64	-1572.32	2685.41
Residual	38	782.84	-551.92	969.41
Total	41	1788.48	-2124.24	3654.82

In this example the adjusted Izod means are of only incidental interest.   We go directly to the adjusted treatment sum of squares, given in Table 7.9.   The

TABLE 7.9

TEST OF EFFICACY OF LOSS IN WEIGHT TO ACCOUNT FOR
TREATMENT EFFECTS

	D.F.	Sum of Squares	Mean Square
Difference of regressions	1	0.19	
Treatments, reduced	2	85.04	
Treatments, adjusted	3	85.23	$28.41^{(n)}$
Residual, reduced	37	468.61	12.67
Total, reduced	40	553.84	

(n) Not significant

analysis shows that the adjusted mean square is not significant, so that weight loss has satisfactorily accounted for the variation in Izod value.   Had the mean square been significant, we could have further analyzed it into terms for difference of regression and reduced variation between treatments.   The purpose of such an analysis would be to see whether the significant adjusted treatment effect could be attributed to a difference of regressions.   If such a difference of regressions exists, it may possibly be interpreted in terms of other factors associated with the loss in weight (for example, deterioration of the remaining wood substance), but varying significantly from one treatment to another.   In the present instance, however, as is shown in Table 7.9, there is no significant difference of regressions even if it were appropriate to carry out the detailed analysis.

7.7 FURTHER APPLICATIONS OF COVARIANCE ANALYSIS

Covariance analysis may readily be applied to the adjustment of data for two or more independent variables.   For each line of the analysis— treatments, residual and total—the reduced sums of squares of the dependent variable are determined.   The analysis is based on these reduced sums of squares.   If there are p independent variables, q degrees of freedom for treatments, and n for total, the resulting comparisons have the following degrees of freedom:

Difference of regressions	p
Treatments, reduced	$q - p$
Residual, reduced	$n - p - q$
Total, reduced	$n - p$

In such an analysis, some of the variables may be environmental and some explanatory. The interpretation of the results of the analysis must take these possibilities into account.

The use of covariance analysis to eliminate a causal or explanatory variable has many applications in statistical work. The method is particularly useful in testing hypotheses. For instance, the hypothesis to be tested may be that the variation of a number of variables between groups is attributable to the variation of one of them or of some compound of them. This question arises in discriminant analysis, where the linear compound of a set of variables that best distinguishes between a number of groups is sought. The linear compound specified by the null hypothesis is then the "explanatory variable"; to test its adequacy as a discriminant function we perform an analysis of covariance and test the significance of the reduced variation in the remaining variables. In the same way, the adequacy of two or more linear compounds to account for the variation of a set of variables may be tested, by eliminating their joint effects by covariance. These questions are discussed fully in Chapter 10, where it is shown that the practically useful tests of significance in multivariate analysis are generalizations of the analysis of covariance.

CHAPTER 8

The Treatment
of Heterogeneous Data

8.1 GENERAL

In previous chapters we have been concerned mainly with the analysis of homogeneous data, that is, data that may be assumed to have been drawn from a single population. Only in Chapter 7, in discussing the analysis of covariance, have we considered data that were divided into groups according to treatment classifications. However, whether the object was to make an adjustment to the dependent variable for the effects of the independent variables, or to find an interpretation of the treatment effect in terms of the independent variables, the purpose of the analysis was to eliminate extraneous sources of variation in determining the relationship. The relationship between the variables was assumed to be the same for each treatment.

When the data are not homogeneous, their interpretation can become complicated. This chapter will deal with a number of different problems which arise with heterogeneous data. Clearly, some such problems would be so special, and their analysis so complicated, as to be outside the scope of this book. Hence only a selection can be given here.

8.2 COMPARISON OF REGRESSION EQUATIONS
FROM INDEPENDENT SETS OF DATA

When measurements have been made of several variables in a number of different sets of data, the question arises whether the same regression relationship will apply to each set. Even if the regression coefficients are equal for each set, the constant terms may differ, so that the regression lines will be parallel rather than coincident. For example, in biological assay, when a compound of unknown strength is being tested against a known standard, varying doses of each are applied, and the organism's response is measured. For each compound, the regression of response on dosage is determined; if a pair of parallel regression lines fits the data satisfactorily, the distance between the lines (measured parallel to the dosage axis) gives the relative potency of the two compounds.

If the regression equations for the different sets are identical, even to the constant term, the sets may be regarded as equivalent with respect to the dependent variable, any differences between the groups being attributable to differences in the values of the independent variables. This case was considered in Chapter 7 in the discussion of explanatory variables.

The significance of the difference among the regression coefficients for different sets may readily be tested, by means of the analysis of variance. On the hypothesis that the regression coefficients in the populations are the same, the common set of coefficients may be estimated from the combined sums of squares and products within the sets, and the regression sum of squares determined from the combined data. This sum of squares would be identical with the sum of the regression sums of squares from each set, if the regression coefficients were in fact the same for each set; hence, the difference between the sum of the regression sums of squares for each set and the combined regression sum of squares gives a criterion appropriate for an over-all test of differences among the coefficients. This is what is generally required. If, however, it is considered to be of interest to compare individual coefficients in the different sets, the significance of their deviations from their weighted mean may be determined.

To carry out these tests we shall require (i) the combined sums of squares and products for the different groups, which we define as the sums of the corresponding sums of squares and products within groups; and (ii) the over-all sums of squares and products, which we define as the total sums of squares and products over all the groups, regardless of group differences. Those familiar with the analysis of variance will recognize that the over-all sums of squares and products exceed the corresponding combined elements by the sums of squares and products between groups.

Suppose that there are m sets of data, with p independent variables $x_1, x_2, \cdots, x_p$. We use the following notation:

n_r number in rth group

n total number

u_r sum of squares of y in the rth set

p_{ri} sum of products with x_i in the rth set

t_{rhi} sum of products of x_h and x_i in the rth set

b_{ri} partial regression coefficient on x_i in the rth set

t_{chi} combined sum of products of x_h and x_i and, similarly, other quantities in the combined analysis will be indicated by the subscript c;

t_{ohi} over-all sum of products of x_h and x_i and, similarly, other quantities in the over-all analysis will be indicated by the subscript o.

(i) Test of Differences among Regression Coefficients (Parallelism)

The sum of squares for regression for the rth set is

$$\sum_i b_{ri} p_{ri}, \qquad \text{with } p \text{ degrees of freedom,}$$

where

$$b_{ri} = \sum_h p_{rh} t_r^{hi}.$$

In the same way, the combined regression coefficients are

$$b_{ci} = \sum_h p_{ch} t_c^{hi},$$

so that the sum of squares for the combined regression, also with p degrees of freedom, is

$$\sum_i b_{ci} p_{ci}.$$

Hence the sum of squares for testing difference of regressions is

$$\sum_r \sum_i b_{ri} p_{ri} - \sum_i b_{ci} p_{ci}, \qquad (8.1)$$

with $(m-1)p$ degrees of freedom.

Since

$$p_{ci} = \sum_r p_{ri},$$

the sum of squares (8.1) may be written in the form

$$\sum_r \sum_i (b_{ri} - b_{ci}) p_{ri},$$

in which its dependence on the differences of the regression coefficients in the different groups is clearly shown.

The analysis of variance for testing difference of regressions is shown in Table 8.1.

TABLE 8.1

	D.F.	Sum of Squares
Combined regression	p	$\sum_i b_{ci} p_{ci}$
Difference of regressions	$(m-1)p$	$\sum_r \sum_i b_{ri} p_{ri} - \sum_i b_{ci} p_{ci}$
Combined residual	$n - mp - m$	$u_c - \sum_r \sum_i b_{ri} p_{ri}$
Total within groups	$n - m$	u_c

It will seldom be required to make more detailed tests of differences among regression coefficients. However, it may sometimes be of interest to determine whether the set of regression coefficients on one of the independent variables contributes significantly to the heterogeneity; this set may then be tested separately. For the comparison of the regression coefficients in different groups for one of the independent variables, we calculate the sum of squares of deviations of these coefficients from their weighted mean.

The weighted mean of the coefficients b_{ri} is

$$\bar{b}_i = \frac{\sum_r b_{ri}/t_r^{ii}}{\sum_r 1/t_r^{ii}} \; ;$$

the sum of squares of deviations is

$$\sum_r (b_{ri} - \bar{b}_i)^2/t_r^{ii}$$

$$= \sum_r (b_{ri}^2/t_r^{ii}) - \bar{b}_i^2 \sum_r (1/t_r^{ii})$$

with $m - 1$ degrees of freedom. This sum of squares may be tested against the combined residual mean square.

(ii) Test of Differences of Position (Coincidence)

If the difference of regressions is not significant, it may be assumed that the regression lines for the different sets are parallel, the combined regression coefficients b_{ci} being applicable. The question then arises whether the differences in the position of these parallel lines are significant. To test this, a single line is fitted to all the data, regardless of group differences. The over-all regression coefficients are

$$b_{oi} = \sum_h p_{oh} t_o^{hi},$$

giving an over-all regression sum of squares of

$$\sum_i b_{oi} p_{oi}.$$

The over-all sum of squares of y has $n - 1$ degrees of freedom, an increase of $m - 1$ degrees of freedom over the total within groups, this increase representing the variation between groups. To derive the adjusted sum of squares between groups, we add to the sum of squares between groups the combined regression sum of squares and deduct the over-all regression sum of squares. As might be expected, this is the same as the derivation of the adjusted sum of squares in covariance analysis, since a test of difference of positions is in fact a test of the means adjusted for the independent variables.

The analysis of variance, in which tests of difference of regression and of position are combined, may be set out as in Table 8.2.   In setting out the tests in this way we should not test difference of positions unless difference of regressions is in fact not significant.

TABLE 8.2

	D.F.	Sum of Squares
Over-all regression	p	$\sum_i b_{oi} p_{oi}$
Difference of positions	$m - 1$	$u_o - u_c - \sum_i b_{oi} p_{oi} + \sum_i b_{ci} p_{ci}$
Difference of regressions	$(m - 1)p$	$\sum_r \sum_i b_{ri} p_{ri} - \sum_i b_{ci} p_{ci}$
Combined residual	$n - mp - m$	$u_c - \sum_r \sum_i b_{ri} p_{ri}$
Total	$n - 1$	u_o

8.3   AN EXAMPLE

Example 8.1   Biological Assay of Oestrogenic Activity of Green Clovers.   Clover (*Trifolium subterraneum* L.) contains a material which acts as an oestrogen.   In order to assess the oestrogenic activity of the clover, and the variation in activity in different strains, Alexander and Watson (1951) took samples of clover of various strains, dried them, and fed them at various levels of daily dose to spayed female guinea pigs.   The animals were killed after two days of the feeding treatments and the uterine weights determined.   The uterine weight was taken as a measure of the oestrogenic activity of the clovers. For the present analysis we use the results for standard clover (a homogeneous sample of dehydrated clover in tablet form) and for clover of the Bacchus Marsh and Dwalganup strains.

If relative potencies of different materials are to be determined (in terms of the ratios of dose levels of different materials giving the same response), it is convenient to express the effect of each as a regression of response on the logarithm of dose (designated "dosage" by Finney).   In this experiment it was found that the regression on dosage was approximately linear, and the residual variances were homogeneous, if log uterine weight was taken as the independent variable. Table 8.3 sets out the results for log daily dose and log uterine weight for each animal, together with log body weight at the beginning of the experiment, which was included in the analysis to provide a correction for the initial variation among the animals.

To test the homogeneity of the regressions, it is necessary to determine the regression equations for each strain and the combined regression coefficients. In Table 8.4 the sums of squares and products necessary for these calculations are given.   In making these calculations, it is desirable to record for each strain the crude sums of squares and products, which will be required for the calculation of the over-all sums of squares and products.   We could include the

TABLE 8.3

RESULTS OF EXPERIMENT ON EFFECT OF DOSE OF CLOVER ON
UTERINE WEIGHT

$x_1 = \log_{10}(\text{daily dose}, g)$
$x_2 = \log_{10}(\text{initial body weight}, g)$
$y = \log_{10}(100 \times \text{uterine weight}, g)$

Standard			Bacchus Marsh			Dwalganup		
x_1	x_2	y	x_1	x_2	y	x_1	x_2	y
1.167	2.690	1.878	1.375	2.708	1.834	1.498	2.699	1.882
1.167	2.665	1.880	1.375	2.681	1.772	1.498	2.690	1.925
1.167	2.663	1.941	1.375	2.672	1.718	1.498	2.672	1.778
1.167	2.643	1.898	1.375	2.655	1.786	1.498	2.653	1.843
1.167	2.613	1.823	1.375	2.643	1.766	1.498	2.643	1.955
			1.375	2.633	1.760	1.498	2.556	1.713
1.025	2.724	1.830	1.236	2.699	1.731	1.350	2.708	1.873
1.025	2.672	1.916	1.236	2.677	1.682	1.350	2.681	1.843
1.025	2.659	1.849	1.236	2.672	1.719	1.350	2.663	1.801
1.025	2.643	1.873	1.236	2.663	1.713	1.350	2.653	1.816
1.025	2.633	1.737	1.236	2.653	1.770	1.350	2.653	1.883
			1.236	2.655	1.665	1.350	2.643	1.818
0.886	2.708	1.827	1.093	2.699	1.708	1.197	2.699	1.854
0.886	2.681	1.865	1.093	2.681	1.639	1.197	2.681	1.772
0.886	2.663	1.757	1.093	2.663	1.747	1.197	2.663	1.810
0.886	2.643	1.785	1.093	2.663˙	1.622	1.197	2.659	1.744
0.886	2.623	1.753	1.093	2.643	1.719	1.197	2.653	1.732
			1.093	2.633	1.665	1.197	2.643	1.751
0.740	2.633	1.713						
0.740	2.699	1.727						
0.740	2.690	1.737						
0.740	2.672	1.740						
0.740	2.653	1.725						
Total								
19.090	53.270	36.254	22.224	47.993	31.016	24.270	47.912	32.793
Mean								
0.954	2.664	1.813	1.235	2.666	1.723	1.348	2.662	1.822

over-all analysis too at this stage, but we prefer to bring it in after the homogeneity of the regressions has been tested. The four inverse matrices and four pairs of regression coefficients (one for each strain, one for the combined analysis) are set out in Table 8.5, together with the regression sum of squares for each. Although the regression coefficients appear rather variable, such variation is possibly due to sampling error. The analysis given in Table 8.6 tests this point.

TABLE 8.4

SUMS OF SQUARES AND PRODUCTS FOR EACH STRAIN AND FOR COMBINED DATA

	Standard (19 D.F.)			Bacchus Marsh (17 D.F.)			Dwalganup (17 D.F.)			Combined (53 D.F.)		
	x_1	x_2	y	x_1	x_2	y	x_1	x_2	y	x_1	x_2	y
	0.504 145	−0.014 654	0.181 384	0.238 588	0.001 453	0.075 459	0.271 828	−0.012 717	0.065 424	1.014 561	−0.025 918	0.322 267
	−0.014 654	0.016 201	0.005 193	0.001 453	0.008 258	0.002 791	−0.012 717	0.019 113	0.018 421	−0.025 918	0.043 572	0.026 405
			0.100 656			0.050 806			0.076 304			0.227 766

TABLE 8.5

INVERSE MATRICES, REGRESSION COEFFICIENTS, AND REGRESSION SUMS OF SQUARES

	Standard		Bacchus Marsh		Dwalganup		Combined	
		b_i		b_i		b_i		b_i
	2.037 115 1.842 60	0.379 07	4.195 822 −0.738 26	0.314 55	3.796 988 2.526 36	0.294 95	1.000 857 0.595 34	0.338 26
	1.842 60 63.391 2	0.663 41	−0.738 26 121.224 6	0.282 63	2.526 36 54.001 3	1.160 04	0.595 34 23.304 6	0.807 22
	Regression sum of squares = 0.072 202		Regression sum of squares = 0.024 524		Regression sum of squares = 0.040 666		Regression sum of squares = 0.130 325	

TABLE 8.6

ANALYSIS OF VARIANCE TO TEST HOMOGENEITY OF REGRESSIONS

	D.F.	Sum of Squares	Mean Square
Combined regression	2	0.130 325	
Difference of regressions	4	0.007 067	$0.001\ 767^{(n)}$
Combined residual	47	0.090 374	0.001 923
Total within groups	53	0.227 766	

[n] Not significant

We see from Table 8.6 that the difference of regressions is not significant, so that it is valid to use the combined regression. We can also test the effect of dose and the efficacy of the adjustment for initial body weight. The standard errors of b_1 and b_2 are

$$\text{S.E. } (b_1) = \sqrt{(0.001\ 923 \times 1.000\ 857)} = 0.044$$
$$\text{S.E. } (b_2) = \sqrt{(0.001\ 923 \times 23.3046)} = 0.21.$$

Both regression coefficients are highly significant, so that the adjustment for body weight has some effect on the relation of uterine weight and dose.

To test the difference of positions of the lines, these differences representing differences in relative potency, we require the over-all analysis of regression effects. The total sums of squares and products are shown in Table 8.7, and the inverse matrix, over-all regression coefficients, and sum of squares in Table 8.8. The analysis to test the difference of positions is shown in Table 8.9. This

TABLE 8.7

TOTAL SUMS OF SQUARES AND PRODUCTS

x_1	x_2	y
$\begin{bmatrix} 2.591\ 015 \\ -0.028\ 235 \end{bmatrix}$	$\begin{bmatrix} -0.028\ 235 \\ 0.043\ 758 \end{bmatrix}$	0.248 958
		0.022 135
		0.336 288

TABLE 8.8

INVERSE MATRIX AND OVER-ALL REGRESSION COEFFICIENTS AND
REGRESSION SUM OF SQUARES

$$b_i$$

$\begin{bmatrix} 0.388\ 682 \\ 0.250\ 80 \end{bmatrix}$	$\begin{bmatrix} 0.250\ 80 \\ 23.014\ 8 \end{bmatrix}$	0.102 32
		0.571 87

Regression sum of squares = 0.038 132

TABLE 8.9

ANALYSIS OF VARIANCE TO TEST HOMOGENEITY OF POSITIONS AND
REGRESSIONS

	D.F.	Sum of Squares	Mean Square
Over-all regression	2	0.038 132	
Difference of positions	2	0.200 715	0.100 4**
Difference of regressions	4	0.007 067	0.001 767[n]
Combined residual	47	0.090 374	0.001 923
Total	55	0.336 288	

[n] Not significant
** Significant at 1 per cent level

analysis could have been carried out by the method shown in Example 7.1, with
the modifications necessary for more than one independent variable.

The difference of positions is highly significant. In this example, there is
really no need to make this test, since the difference of positions represents
potency differences that are already known to exist. The analysis has been
given in order to show the method.

The three regression equations, based on the combined regression, are

Standard: $\qquad Y = -0.659 + 0.338x_1 + 0.807x_2$

Bacchus Marsh: $\quad Y = -0.846 + 0.338x_1 + 0.807x_2$

Dwalganup: $\qquad Y = -0.782 + 0.338x_1 + 0.807x_2.$

Hence the potencies R of each strain relative to the standard are estimated as
follows:

Bacchus Marsh: $\quad \log R = (-0.846 + 0.659)/0.338$

$= -0.553$

$R = \quad 0.280$

Dwalganup: $\qquad \log R = (-0.782 + 0.659)/0.338$

$= -0.364$

$R = \quad 0.433.$

The two strains considered have potencies between a quarter and a half that
of the standard. If desired, fiducial limits for the relative potencies may be
derived by the methods given in Chapter 6.

8.4 MORE DETAILED COMPARISONS AMONG REGRESSION EQUATIONS—CONCURRENCE OF REGRESSION LINES

The comparisons so far given in this chapter have involved straightforward applications of regression methods. Occasionally more elaborate

comparisons are required. Sometimes a set of regression lines, rather than being parallel, appear to be concurrent. This type of effect is likely to occur, for example, when different materials produce a different rate of response, whereas all give the same response at some fixed level. This level in practice is often not zero and is generally not exactly known. When three or more regression lines are concurrent, it is possible to measure the difference between the effects of different materials or treatments by means of the ratios of the distances between the lines, measured along an ordinate. It will be seen that parallel regression lines are simply a special case of concurrent lines; in fact, the ratio of the effectiveness of different materials may be measured in the same way as for concurrent lines, that is, by the distances between the intercepts on a transversal.

For a discussion of the fitting of concurrent regression lines, reference may be made to the papers of Tocher (1952) and Williams (1953). These papers do not, however, present the method of analysis in as convenient a form as that given here. The method given here, basing the tests of significance on the analysis of covariance, is new.

We shall denote the point of concurrence of the lines by (ξ, η). When this point is known, the problem is amenable to standard methods, for regression lines through a given point are fitted in the same way as a regression line through the origin, as described in Chapter 2. When the ordinate η is unknown, some more detail is required, as will now be shown.

Suppose that as before there are m groups, that there are n values in each group, and that the values of the independent variable x are the same for each group.

We shall require the following notation:

Unrestricted	y_r	value of y in rth group
regression	$\bar{y}_r$	mean of y for rth group
	p_r	sum of products of x and y from rth group
	t_r	sum of squares of x (the same for each group)
	b_r	regression coefficient for rth group
	$\bar{p}$	$\sum_r p_r/m$
	$\bar{b}$	$\sum_r b_r/m$
Concurrent	p_r'	$Sy_r(x - \xi)$
regression	t_r'	$S(x - \xi)^2$
	b_r'	regression coefficient for rth concurrent line
	$\bar{p}'$	$\sum_r p_r'/m$

x_c, y_c estimated coordinates of point of concurrence

$J \qquad n \sum_r (\bar{y}_r - \bar{y})^2$

$K \qquad \dfrac{n}{t_r} \sum_r \bar{y}_r (p_r - \bar{p})$

$L \qquad \dfrac{n}{t_r^2} \sum_r (p_r - \bar{p})^2$

When the ordinate of concurrence η is unknown, it may be estimated by noting that, in this case, the point of concurrence will be on the mean regression line for all the data. The mean regression line is

$$Y = \bar{y} + \bar{b}(x - \bar{x});$$

hence, the estimate of η is given by

$$y_c = \bar{y} + \bar{b}(\xi - \bar{x}).$$

If ξ is also unknown, an estimate is to be substituted.

Once y_c is determined, the restricted regression coefficients are readily found. We have

$$b_r' = S(y_r - y_c)(x - \xi)/S(x - \xi)^2$$
$$= [p_r' + ny_c(\xi - \bar{x})]/t_r'.$$

In assessing the fit of concurrent regression lines, there are several aspects to be tested. In comparing regression lines for several sets of data, as shown in Section 8.2, the usual approach is to examine, first, whether the slopes of the lines differ significantly, and second, whether, if the slopes are assumed not to differ, the distances between the parallel lines fitted to the data differ significantly. Each of these comparisons has $m - 1$ degrees of freedom. For the present purpose, these two aspects are viewed in a different way. The comparisons required are set out in Table 8.10. These comparisons are tested in order, just as the difference

TABLE 8.10

	D.F.
Mean regression	1
Ordinate of concurrence	1
Difference of concurrent regressions	$m - 1$
Departure from concurrence, for given abscissa	$m - 1$
Total variation due to regressions	$2m$

of slopes needs to be tested before the distances between the lines are examined. Departure from concurrence is tested first; if this is significant, no choice of point of concurrence will give a satisfactory fit to the data.

The sum of squares for concurrent regressions, given by the first three items in the table above, has $m + 1$ degrees of freedom, since m regression coefficients and the ordinate of concurrence have been fitted. This sum of squares is found to be

$$\frac{\sum\limits_r p_r'^2}{t_r'} + \frac{y_c^2 mnt_r}{t_r'}.$$

Of the two parts, the first represents the regressions through the point $(\xi, 0)$, and the second the departure of y_c from zero. In most applications it would be more appropriate to take the two parts as the regression through (ξ, η), and the departure of y_c from η, where η is some hypothetical value of the ordinate. Thus, to test the significance of the departure of y_c from η, the appropriate sum of squares is

$$\frac{(y_c - \eta)^2 mnt_r}{t_r'}.$$

This is exactly analogous to the sum of squares for testing the significance of the constant term in a regression equation.

From the form of the first part (the sum of squares for the regressions through a given point), we see that the sum of squares for the difference of concurrent regressions, with $m - 1$ degrees of freedom, is given by

$$\frac{\sum\limits_r (p_r' - \bar{p}')^2}{t_r'}.$$

For purposes of calculation and significance testing, it is advantageous to express this sum of squares in terms of quantities independent of ξ, namely J, K, and L defined in the list of notation. We find that the sum of squares for difference of concurrent regressions equals

$$\frac{1}{t_r'}\left[n(\xi - \bar{x})^2 J - 2(\xi - \bar{x})t_r K + \frac{t_r^2 L}{n} \right].$$

Departures from concurrence are measured by the variation among the m quantities,

$$y_{rc} = \bar{y}_r + b_r(\xi - \bar{x}) = \bar{y}_r + p_r(\xi - \bar{x})/t_r,$$

which are the ordinates of the unrestricted regression lines at $x = \xi$, and whose mean is y_c.

Since the variance of each of these quantities is proportional to

$$\frac{t_r'}{nt_r},$$

the sum of squares for departure from concurrence is

$$\frac{nt_r}{t_r'} \left(\sum_r y_{rc}^2 - m y_c^2 \right)$$

$$= \frac{t_r}{t_r'} [J + 2(\xi - \bar{x})K + (\xi - \bar{x})^2 L]$$

with $m - 1$ degrees of freedom.

The analysis of variance is set out in Table 8.11.

TABLE 8.11

	D.F.	Sum of Squares
Mean regression	1	$m\bar{p}'^2/t_r'$
Ordinate of concurrence	1	$mnt_r y_c^2/t_r'$
Difference of concurrent regressions	$m - 1$	$\sum_r (p_r' - \bar{p}')^2/t_r' =$
		$\dfrac{1}{t_r'}\left[n(\xi - \bar{x})^2 J - 2(\xi - \bar{x})t_r K + \dfrac{t_r^2}{n} L \right]$
Departure from concurrence for given abscissa	$m - 1$	$\dfrac{t_r}{t_r'}[J + 2(\xi - \bar{x})K + (\xi - \bar{x})^2 L]$
Total variation due to regressions	$2m$	$\dfrac{1}{t_r'}(m\bar{p}'^2 + mnt_r y_c^2) + J + \dfrac{t_r L}{n}$
Residual	$m(n - 2)$	by difference
Total (uncorrected)	mn	$\sum_r S(y_r^2)$

The sum of the first two terms in this analysis equals the correction for the mean plus the usual sum of squares for mean regression, namely

$$mn\bar{y}^2 + mt_r\bar{b}^2.$$

In the table it is split up in a different manner in order to show the term for testing the significance of a hypothetical value of the ordinate of concurrence. Again, the residual sum of squares is simply the sum of the residual sums of squares from the individual regressions and would generally be so determined.

Although it is not necessary for the present analysis, in which ξ is given, it is instructive, and will also be of use later on, to frame the significance tests given here in terms of an analysis of covariance.

The analysis of the variation between regression lines is really an analysis of two variables, $\bar{y}_r$ and p_r, which are statistically independent, and whose variances are in the known ratio $1/n : t_r$. It can be shown that, since ξ is given as the abscissa of concurrence, the variate b_r' (which is a linear combination of $\bar{y}_r$ and p_r, involving ξ) is the explanatory variable, in terms of which the variation of either $\bar{y}_r$ or p_r can be interpreted. Actually, since

$$b_r' = [p_r' + ny_c(\xi - \bar{x})]/t_r',$$

in this example p_r' is equivalent to b_r' as a covariance variable and will for convenience be used in the analysis.

Now since $\bar{y}_r$ and p_r are statistically independent, the sum of squares for their joint variation, with $2(m - 1)$ degrees of freedom, is

$$n \sum_r (\bar{y}_r - \bar{y})^2 + \sum_r (p_r - \bar{p})^2/t_r$$

$$= J + \frac{t_r L}{n}.$$

The sum of squares for p_r' is likewise

$$\sum_r (p_r' - \bar{p}')^2/t_r' = \frac{1}{t_r'} \left[n(\xi - \bar{x})^2 J - 2(\xi - \bar{x})t_r K + \frac{t_r^2}{n} L \right],$$

so that deduction of the sum of squares for p_r' leaves a remainder

$$\frac{t_r}{t_r'} [J + 2(\xi - \bar{x})K + (\xi - \bar{x})^2 L], \qquad (8.2)$$

with $m - 1$ degrees of freedom.

This remainder may alternatively be derived by transforming from $\bar{y}_r$ and p_r to new independent variables

$$p_r' = p_r - n(\xi - \bar{x})\bar{y}_r$$

and
$$y_{rc} = b_r(\xi - \bar{x}) + \bar{y}_r.$$

Now p_r' and y_{rc} are independent, so the sum of squares for regression of y_{rc} on p_r' should be distributed accordingly. If the regression is significant, it reflects on the adequacy of p_r' as an explanatory covariance variable, and hence on the given value of ξ. Hence, if we regard ξ not as given but as unknown, we may derive fiducial limits by determining that range of values of ξ for which the regression of y_{rc} on p_r' is not significant. For this reason we shall call this sum of squares for regression the sum of squares for the abscissa of concurrence. Of course, this determination is valid only if the residual variation of y_{rc}, which measures departures from concurrence, is not significant. If there are significant departures from concurrence, no set of concurrent lines is satisfactory.

The difference between the analysis of covariance here given and that usually described is that here we have variates whose variances and

covariances are known (apart from a constant factor), so that the population regression of one on the other can be determined.   Then the sum of
squares for regression of y_{rc} on p_r' is really the sum of squares for the
difference between the population regression (which vanishes for these two
variables) and the sample regression.

This analysis has been described in terms of y_{rc} and p_r'; however, since
each is a linear function of $\bar{y}_r$ and p_r, the same result would have been
obtained if the regression of, say, $\bar{y}_r$ on p_r' had been determined, provided
we deduct the population regression coefficient of $\bar{y}_r$ on p_r', which is found
to be

$$(\xi - \bar{x})/t_r'.$$

The most useful method of calculating the regression sum of squares is
by expressing it in terms of the quantities J, K, and L previously given,
which are independent of ξ.   We have

$$\sum_r y_{rc}(p_r' - \bar{p}') = -\left[(\xi - \bar{x})^2 K - (\xi - \bar{x})\left(\frac{t_r}{n}L - J\right) - \frac{t_r}{n}K\right]$$

$$\sum_r (p_r' - \bar{p}')^2 = n(\xi - \bar{x})^2 J - 2(\xi - \bar{x})t_r K + \frac{t_r^2}{n}L.$$

Hence the regression sum of squares (sum of squares for abscissa) equals

$$\frac{nt_r\left[(\xi - \bar{x})^2 K - (\xi - \bar{x})\left(\frac{t_r}{n}L - J\right) - \frac{t_r}{n}K\right]^2}{t_r'\left[n(\xi - \bar{x})^2 J - 2(\xi - \bar{x})t_r K + \frac{t_r^2}{n}L\right]}.$$

We have thus arrived indirectly at a means of testing the concordance
of the data with a given value of ξ.   Now the sum of squares for the
ordinate of concurrence is a criterion for testing the concordance of η
with the data, conditional on the given value of ξ.   Taken together with
the sum of squares for abscissa of concurrence, this enables the concordance
of ξ and η jointly with the data to be tested.

The two sums of squares for the joint test are seen to be sums of squares
of the y_{rc}, one being for the departure of their mean y_c from η, the other
being for regression on p_r'.   Thus the tests of significance of the position
of the point of concurrence reduce to an analysis of variance of y_{rc}, and
the test for departure from concurrence is based on its residual sum of
squares.

These significance tests enable fiducial limits for ξ and η to be found,
and we have also shown how η may be estimated.   To estimate ξ, we
equate to zero the sum of squares for abscissa, or, more simply, the sum of

products of p_r' and y_{rc}. This gives a quadratic equation, one of whose roots maximizes the sum of squares for departure from concurrence, whereas the other minimizes it. From general regression theory it can be shown that the sum of squares for departure from concurrence, being the residual sum of squares from a regression, is given by the ratio

$$\frac{\dfrac{t_r}{n}(JL - K^2)}{\dfrac{1}{t_r'}\sum_r (p_r' - \bar{p}')^2}.$$

Since the numerator is independent of ξ, it follows that the ratio is minimized when the denominator, which is the sum of squares for difference of concurrent regressions, is maximized, and vice versa. Thus, in estimating ξ, the appropriate value to choose is the one that maximizes difference of regressions and minimizes departure from concurrence.

If we put $x_c - \bar{x} = z$, the equation for z is

$$z^2 K - z\left(\frac{t_r}{n}L - J\right) - \frac{t_r}{n}K = 0,$$

giving

$$z = \frac{\dfrac{t_r}{n}L - J \pm \sqrt{\left[\left(J + \dfrac{t_r}{n}L\right)^2 - \dfrac{4t_r}{n}(JL - K^2)\right]}}{2K}.$$

The roots of the equation are real, as is apparent from geometrical considerations.

Table 8.12 shows the relevant sums of squares resulting from the analysis of the y_{rc}.

TABLE 8.12

	D.F.	Calculation of Sum of Squares
Ordinate of concurrence	1	$\dfrac{mnt_r}{t_r'}[\bar{y} + \bar{b}(\xi - \bar{x}) - \eta]^2$
Abscissa of concurrence	1	$\dfrac{nt_r\left[(\xi - \bar{x})^2 K - (\xi - \bar{x})\left(\dfrac{t_r}{n}L - J\right) - \dfrac{t_r K}{n}\right]^2}{t_r'\left[n(\xi - \bar{x})^2 J - 2(\xi - \bar{x})t_r K + \dfrac{t_r^2 L}{n}\right]}$
Departure from concurrence	$m - 2$	$\dfrac{t_r t_r'(JL - K^2)}{n\left[n(\xi - \bar{x})^2 J - 2(\xi - \bar{x})t_r K + \dfrac{t_r^2 L}{n}\right]}$
Total	m	$\dfrac{nt_r}{t_r'}\sum_r [\bar{y}_r - b_r(\xi - \bar{x}) - \eta]^2$

From the foregoing it can be seen that the fitting and testing of concurrent lines may also be carried out in the general case, when the number of observations and their values vary from group to group. For given ξ, the y_{rc} may be determined for each group; since their variances differ, a weighted analysis would be employed. The departures from concurrence would be tested by the weighted sum of squares of departures of the y_{rc} from their weighted mean, and the ordinate of concurrence by the difference between the weighted mean and the hypothetical value η. However, in the general case it is not possible to define an explanatory variable, so that an exact test for the abscissa of concurrence cannot be made in the way just shown.

8.5 AN EXAMPLE OF CONCURRENT REGRESSIONS

Example 8.2   The Fitting of Concurrent Regression Lines to the Relationship between Burst Strength and Basis Weight of Paper Made under Different Conditions.   In a study of the effect of basis weight on the properties of laboratory-made sheets of paper, three batches of pulp were taken and beaten in the Lampen mill for different lengths of time.   From each batch, sheets of six different basis weights were then made, and mechanical tests carried out on them.   The burst strength results from this experiment are set out in Table 8.13, together with values calculated from them.

TABLE 8.13

BURST STRENGTH RESULTS

Basis Weight	x	Beating (revolutions of Lampen Mill)			Total
		1125 $r = 1$	4500 $r = 2$	12,730 $r = 3$	
10	−5	1.73	1.98	3.11	
20	−3	4.99	9.69	12.83	
30	−1	8.74	17.26	22.69	
40	1	12.60	24.52	32.45	
50	3	17.04	31.36	48.22	
60	5	21.18	43.29	59.94	
$6\bar{y}_r$		66.28	128.10	179.24	373.62
p_r		137.26	278.82	400.08	816.16

A preliminary analysis, as given in Table 8.14, shows that the three regression lines of burst strength on basis weight depart significantly from the origin.

The sum of squares for the mean regression (including departure from the origin) is

$$\frac{373.62^2}{18} + \frac{816.16^2}{210} = 10,927.092,$$

so that the sum of squares for difference among regressions, with four degrees of freedom, is

$$12,487.960 - 10,927.092 = 1,560.868.$$

Clearly this is highly significant, so that the lines differ in position or slope or possibly in both.

TABLE 8.14

TEST OF DEPARTURE OF REGRESSION LINES FROM ORIGIN

	D.F.	Sum of Squares	Mean Square
Correction for mean	3	8,821.604	
Regression through means	3	3,666.356	
Sum	6	12,487.960	
Regressions through origin	3	12,311.932	
Departure from origin	3	176.028	58.676**
Residual	12	28.554	2.3795

** Significant at 1 per cent level.

In order to compare the trends for different amounts of beating it would be desirable to base the comparison on regression lines through some common point other than the origin, if such a model were concordant with the data. The common point would represent the basis weight for which the value of burst factor was independent of beating. The ordinate as well as the abscissa of this point will be estimated.

For the independent variable we have taken

$$x = \frac{\text{basis weight} - 35}{5},$$

as shown in the second column of Table 8.13. Its sum of squares is

$$t_r = 70.$$

From the data in Table 8.13 we find

$$m = 3$$
$$n = 6$$
$$J = 1066.499$$
$$K = 212.5744$$
$$L = 42.37452$$
$$JL - K^2 = 4.51.$$

Also
$$\bar{y} = 20.76$$

and
$$\bar{b} = 816.16/210$$
$$= 3.886,$$

so that
$$y_c = 20.76 + 3.886\xi.$$

The sums of squares, in terms of the unknown ξ and η, are set out in the analysis of variance given in Table 8.15. We need first to test departure from concurrence. This sum of squares takes its minimum value 0.034 when ξ has its optimum value -5.02. By comparison with the residual mean square 2.3795 (Table 8.14), this sum of squares is not significant, nor does it attain a significant value for any value of ξ acceptable as an abscissa of concurrence. Hence the fitting of concurrent regression lines to the data is valid.

TABLE 8.15

SUMS OF SQUARES REQUIRED FOR TESTS OF CONCURRENT
REGRESSIONS

	D.F.	Sum of Squares
Ordinate of concurrence	1	$\dfrac{1{,}260(20.76 + 3.886\xi - \eta)^2}{70 + 6\xi^2}$
Abscissa of concurrence	1	$\dfrac{420(212.5744\xi^2 + 572.130\xi - 2{,}480.035)^2}{(70 + 6\xi^2)(6{,}398.994\xi^2 - 29{,}760.42\xi + 34{,}605.86)}$
Departure from concurrence	1	$\dfrac{52.6(70 + 6\xi^2)}{6{,}398.994\xi^2 - 29{,}760.42\xi + 34{,}605.86}$

The point of concurrence is estimated by equating to zero the sums of squares for ordinate and abscissa of concurrence. The value of the abscissa which minimizes departure from concurrence is the appropriate one to take, and the ordinate is the corresponding point on the mean regression line. We find

$$x_c = -5.02$$

$$y_c = 1.26.$$

In order to determine the region in which the point of concurrence may lie, we consider the sums of squares for ordinate and abscissa of concurrence, which we may denote by O and A respectively. Then, on the null hypothesis that ξ and η are the coordinates of the point of concurrence, the ratio

$$\frac{O + A}{2 \times 2.3795}$$

is distributed as F with two and twelve degrees of freedom. Since the 1 per cent point of this distribution is 6.9266, the 99 per cent fiducial region for the point of concurrence is defined by the inequality

$$O + A \leq 4.7590 \times 6.9266$$
$$= 32.964.$$

Using the values of O and A given in Table 8.15, we have calculated the fiducial boundary. This is plotted in Figure 8.1, together with the concurrent regression lines.

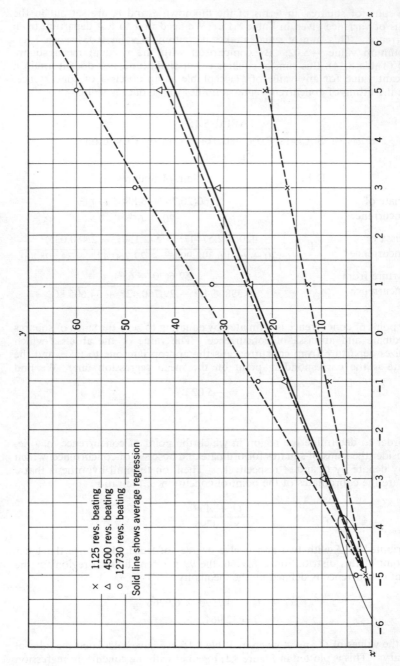

Figure 8.1. Concurrent regressions of burst strength on basis weight of paper, from pulp beaten for different periods, showing 99 per cent fiducial boundary for point of concurrence.

Of particular interest are the maximum ranges for ξ and η. The maximum range for ξ is given when η does not depart from the value given by the mean regression line, so that

$$A \leq 32.964,$$

giving
$$\xi = -7.0 \text{ and } -3.7.$$

The maximum range for η is given when ξ takes its optimum value -5.02, so that

$$O \leq 32.964;$$

negative values being inadmissible, the limits for η are found to be 0.0 and 3.7.

8.6 PROPORTIONALITY OF REGRESSION LINES

An interesting problem whose solution is similar to that of fitting concurrent regression lines is fitting proportional regressions. Suppose, for example, that different properties of a coal, such as carbon content, sulphur content, and calorific value, are linearly related to its ash content. It might be expected that, if the ash consisted of admixed impurities, its proportionate effect would be a simple percentage reduction, the same for each of the properties. Hence, if for the jth property the regression equation on percentage ash were

$$Y_j = a_j + b_j x,$$

we should expect b_j/a_j to be in the neighborhood of $-1/100$. In general, if the theoretical value of the ratio were $-1/\xi$, we could write the regression equations

$$Y_j = b_j(x - \xi),$$

and would then be interested in testing, first, the constancy of ξ for the different variables, and second, the acceptability of various values of ξ. We note that these equations are similar to those in the concurrent regression problem, except that here η vanishes. Also, whereas in fitting concurrent regressions the data were independent groups of the same variable, here they are different variables, possibly correlated.

We shall suppose that there are m different variables y_j, and that the variances and covariances, either known or estimated, are proportional to the elements of a matrix V with typical element v_{jk}.

The tests of proportionality are based on the analysis of the variate

$$y_{jc} = \bar{y}_j + b_j(\xi - \bar{x}),$$

which has expected value zero.

The explanatory variate is, as with concurrent regression,

$$p_j' = Sy_j(x - \xi)$$
$$= p_j - n\bar{y}_j(\xi - \bar{x}).$$

We now define the quantities

$$J = n\sum_j \sum_k v^{jk}\bar{y}_j\bar{y}_k$$

$$K = \frac{n}{t_r}\sum_j \sum_k v^{jk}\bar{y}_j p_k$$

$$L = \frac{n}{t_r^2}\sum_j \sum_k v^{jk}p_j p_k$$

each with m degrees of freedom. Then the sum of squares of the y_{jc} is

$$\frac{t_r}{t_r'}[J + 2(\xi - \bar{x})K + (\xi - \bar{x})^2 L] \tag{8.3}$$

with m degrees of freedom, whereas the sum of squares for regression of y_{jc} on p_j' is

$$\frac{nt_r\left[(\xi - \bar{x})^2 K - (\xi - \bar{x})\left(\dfrac{t_r}{n}L - J\right) - \dfrac{t_r}{n}K\right]^2}{t_r'\left[n(\xi - \bar{x})^2 J - 2(\xi - \bar{x})t_r K + \dfrac{t_r^2}{n}L\right]}. \tag{8.4}$$

We shall call this latter the sum of squares for the constant of proportionality. The residual sum of squares of y_{jc}, measuring departure from proportionality, is found to be

$$\frac{\dfrac{t_r}{n}(JL - K^2)}{\dfrac{1}{t_r'}\sum_j \sum_k v^{jk}p_j' p_k'} \tag{8.5}$$

with $m - 1$ degrees of freedom.

If the v_{jk} are known population variances and covariances, the test of significance is immediate. If they are known apart from a constant factor, that factor can be estimated from the residual sums of squares and products of the variables. If, however, as is more likely, the v_{jk} are themselves the residual sums of squares and products from the unrestricted regressions, each based on $n - 2$ degrees of freedom, the sum of squares of y_{jc} (8.3) is distributed as the ratio of two sums of squares, with m and $n - m - 1$ degrees of freedom. Likewise the regression sum of squares (8.4) and the residual sum of squares (8.5) are distributed as ratios of sums of squares with $1, n - m - 1$ and $m - 1, n - m - 1$ degrees of freedom respectively. Hence we may set up the analysis of variance given in Table 8.16.

The analysis enables us to test a given value of the constant of proportionality, or to set fiducial limits for it, provided, of course, that departure from proportionality is not significant. The constant of proportionality is estimated by equating the sum of products of y_{jc} and p_j' to zero. Since other details are the same as for concurrent regression,

TABLE 8.16

	D.F.	Sum of Squares
Constant of proportionality	1	(8.4)
Departure from proportionality	$m - 1$	(8.5)
Error	$n - m - 1$	1
	$n - 1$	

$$\frac{1 + \dfrac{nt_r}{t_r'} \displaystyle\sum_j \sum_k v^{jk} y_{jc} y_{kc}}{\left| v_{jk} + \dfrac{nt_r}{t_r'} y_{jc} y_{kc} \right|} = \frac{}{|v_{jk}|}$$

they are not discussed further here. In other contexts, an analysis similar to this one will provide a test for the constancy of a set of ratios and fiducial limits for their common expected value.

8.7 THE COMPARISON OF REGRESSION EQUATIONS FROM SETS OF CORRELATED DATA

In all these examples, the different samples have been independent, so that comparisons between them can be made directly. For certain data, however, correlations exist between the sets, usually because each of the variables is affected by some extraneous variable. Yates (1939b) considers the case in which the variables in the different sets are annual values, so that correlations may be expected among them, and he sets up a suitable model and derives a test of significance. Carter (1949) considers the case in which the corresponding values of the variables in different sets are related through an additive constant. Example 8.3 presents some data for which his specification of the problem is appropriate. Besides these two specifications, there are other possibilities; in any particular problem, care is needed to see whether the data obtained follow one of the models given above, or whether some other is needed. A very general discussion has been given by Kullback and Rosenblatt (1957).

Carter's method will often apply, for example, to data in a double classification (the classes of which may be designated groups and treatments), wherein values of the independent variables vary from group to group, and it is of interest to compare the regressions at different treatment levels, group effects having been eliminated. It is readily seen that the analysis of variance can be applied; the effects of groups and treatments need first to be eliminated, and then the regressions may be determined on the residual sums of squares and products. This is in fact what Carter's method reduces to, although in his exposition the derivation is set out in a different way.

In a recent experiment on the water absorption of a fibrous board material, a number of specimens were soaked in water for varying times, and the gains in thickness and weight recorded. It was of interest to determine the relation between these two properties and to test whether the regression coefficients differed significantly for different times. Now for each time, only a regression between specimens could be determined; but these cannot be validly compared without some allowance being made for the correlation introduced by the fact that each regression was based on the same specimens. It is assumed that the specimen differences introduce an additive effect which can be eliminated by deducting the specimen means from each of the values for the specimen.

The question might be raised whether we do in fact want to compare the residual regressions or the between-specimen regressions for different times. It is true that, if the experiment is carried out for only one time, we can determine only a regression between specimens, and that this regression will be of practical value in predicting gain in thickness from gain in weight. However, if our assumption is correct that specimen effects are additive, it is appropriate to base the comparison of regressions on residual variation. The regression between specimens will still be appropriate for prediction at any one time, however. If the assumption of additivity cannot be maintained, some method of analysis such as Yates's, which assumes a more general form of correlation introduced by group effects (in this case, specimen differences) is needed.

Without going into the derivation of the method, we give the normal equations for the regression coefficients.

The comparison is based on an analysis of the residual sum of squares for the dependent variable. The reduction in this sum of squares, due to the fitting of a separate regression coefficient for each set, is compared with that resulting from the fitting of a single regression for the residual variation. Since the separate regression coefficients are correlated, this factor needs to be allowed for in the analysis.

We consider data in m sets, with n results in each set. The notation is as follows:

t_{rs} sum of products of x values in rth and sth sets

p_{rs} sum of products of x values in rth set with y values in sth set

u_{rs} sum of products of y values in rth and sth sets

$$t_{rs}' = \left(\delta_{rs} - \frac{1}{m}\right) t_{rs}$$

$$p_{rs}' = \left(\delta_{rs} - \frac{1}{m}\right) p_{rs}$$

$$u_{rs}' = \left(\delta_{rs} - \frac{1}{m}\right) u_{rs}$$

where $\delta_{rs} = \begin{cases} 1 & r = s \\ 0 & r \neq s \end{cases}$.

It is readily verified that $\sum_r \sum_s t_{rs}'$, $\sum_r \sum_s p_{rs}'$, and $\sum_r \sum_s u_{rs}'$ give the residual sums of squares and products of x and y.

If b_r is the residual regression coefficient for the rth set, then

$$\sum_s b_s t_{rs}' = \sum_s p_{rs}' = p_r'. \qquad (r = 1, 2, \cdots, m)$$

The solutions of these equations are

$$b_s = \sum_r t'^{rs} p_r' \qquad (r = 1, 2, \cdots, m)$$

and the sum of squares for regression, with m degrees of freedom, is

$$\sum_r b_r p_r'.$$

If a single regression coefficient b is fitted to the data, then

$$b = \sum_r \sum_s p_{rs}' / \sum_r \sum_s t_{rs}'$$

which is in fact the ratio of the residual sum of products to the residual sum of squares of x; the corresponding sum of squares is found by standard methods.

The analysis then takes the form shown in Table 8.17.

TABLE 8.17

	D.F.	Sum of Squares
Mean residual regression	1	$b\sum_r p_r'$
Difference of regressions	$m - 1$	by difference
Separate regressions	m	$\sum_r b_r p_r'$
Residual, reduced	$(n-1)(m-1) - m$	by difference
Residual	$(n-1)(m-1)$	$\sum_r \sum_s u_{rs}'$

Example 8.3 The Relationship between Gain in Thickness and Gain in Weight of "Pinex" Hardboard, Soaked in Water for Various Times. In this experiment, on studying the sorption properties of various cellulosic materials, eleven specimens of "Pinex" hardboard were soaked in water. The gains in thickness (y) and in weight (x) were measured after 2, 24, and 48 hours and recorded as percentages of initial weight and thickness. It was of interest to find the residual regression of y on x, and to determine whether the regression relationship varied at different times.

The original data are presented in Table 8.18. Table 8.19 sets out the straightforward analysis of covariance of the data, which is, of course, carried out on the assumption that the residual regressions are equal.

TABLE 8.18

"PINEX" HARDBOARD: PERCENTAGE GAINS IN WEIGHT (x) AND IN THICKNESS (y) AFTER SOAKING

Time

Specimen No.	2 hr.		24 hr.		48 hr.		Total	
	y	x	y	x	y	x	y	x
1	8	13	19	35	21	40	48	88
2	6	11	16	30	17	34	39	75
3	7	10	18	29	21	36	46	75
4	6	8	18	26	19	33	43	67
5	5	7	14	20	18	27	37	54
6	7	11	17	31	18	36	42	78
7	8	14	18	37	20	44	46	95
8	9	15	23	41	23	46	55	102
9	3	6	13	22	15	30	31	58
10	8	12	17	32	20	39	45	83
11	8	11	17	32	20	38	45	81
Total	75	118	190	335	212	403	477	856

TABLE 8.19

ANALYSIS OF COVARIANCE

		Sums of Squares and Products			y, Adjusted for x		
	D.F.	y^2	yx	x^2	D.F.	Sum of Squares	Mean Square
Specimens	10	130.18	264.24	704.55			
Times	2	984.18	1984.73	4028.42	2	13.06	6.53**
$S \times T$	20	15.82	14.94	76.91	19	12.92	0.680
Total	32	1130.18	2263.91	4809.88			

** Significant at 1 per cent level.

TABLE 8.20

MATRICES OF SUMS OF SQUARES AND PRODUCTS OF RESULTS IN
TABLE 8.18, AND CALCULATIONS FOR TESTING THE DIFFERENCES
BETWEEN RESIDUAL REGRESSIONS

	t_{rs}				p_{rs}	
r \ s	1	2	3	r \ s	1	2	3
1	80.18	171.36	151.91	1	44.45	59.82	46.82
2	171.36	382.73	342.82	2	94.91	138.64	102.64
3	151.91	342.82	318.55	3	85.27	124.09	96.09

Sum of elements: 2113.64

= 3 × sum of squares for specimens

r \ s	1	t_{rs}' 2	3	p_r'
1	53.45	−57.12	−50.64	−5.91
2	−57.12	255.15	−114.27	26.58
3	−50.64	−114.27	212.36	−5.73
				14.94

Sum of elements: 76.90

= residual sum of squares

Inverse Matrix: t'^{rs} Regression Coefficients b_r

$$10^{-6} \times \begin{bmatrix} 216,514 & 94,325 & 102,386 \\ 94,325 & 46,256 & 47,383 \\ 102,386 & 47,383 & 54,621 \end{bmatrix}$$

0.6409
0.4005
0.3414

Mean regression   0.1943

TABLE 8.21

ANALYSIS OF RESIDUAL VARIANCE, TO TEST DIFFERENCES AMONG
RESIDUAL REGRESSIONS

	D.F.	Sum of Squares	Mean Square
Mean residual regression	1	2.90	2.90*
Difference of regressions	2	2.00	1.00[n]
Separate regressions	3	4.90	
Residual, reduced	17	10.92	0.6424
Residual	20	15.82	

[n] Not significant.
* Significant at 5 per cent level.

In Table 8.20 the calculations for deriving the residual regressions are shown. The three residual regression coefficients are derived in the usual way. The mean regression coefficient is smaller than any of the individual coefficients because of the negative correlations among the residuals.

The analysis of variance in Table 8.21 shows that the residual regressions are not significantly different.

8.8   CALCULATION OF AN OVER-ALL REGRESSION COEFFICIENT FROM HETEROGENEOUS DATA

A number of sets of data, or a single set of heterogeneous data, will often provide several estimates of a regression coefficient. We have already discussed, in Section 8.2, the comparison and combination of regression coefficients from a number of sets of similar data. In other cases, although the principles are the same, the procedure is not quite so straightforward. For example, maximum compressive strength and density measurements may be made on a number of specimens of a species of timber. In general, for reasons of practical convenience, such a sample will not be drawn directly at random from the population, but in at least two stages: first, a sample of trees will be selected, and then from each tree will be taken a sample of specimens. Then an analysis of variance and covariance can be carried out on the data. The regression of maximum compressive strength on density may be determined from two sources, the sums of squares and products between trees and the sums of squares and products within trees. If the regression coefficients differ substantially, a test of significance is needed to establish the reality of the difference, but, if the difference is not significant, a combined regression coefficient, suitably weighted, is needed. The weights for this combined regression coefficient would be inversely proportional to the estimated variances of the two coefficients.

Sometimes, however, even when the regression coefficients between trees and within trees differ significantly, some combined coefficient is required to represent the relationship that would be found in random sampling from the species. Then the weighting would be not inversely proportional to the estimated variances but such as to simulate the results that would be achieved by random sampling. It is often found, however, that this weighted regression coefficient differs little from the over-all regression coefficient derived from the total line of the analysis without regard to differences between trees, as shown in the following example.

If m trees are sampled, the number of specimens from the rth tree being n_r, totaling n in all, we have the following analysis of variance and covariance:

	D.F.	y^2	xy	x^2
Between trees	$m-1$	u_b	p_b	t_b
Within trees	$n-m$	u_c	p_c	t_c
Total	$n-1$	u_o	p_o	t_o

The regression coefficient from the within-trees line, for example, would be

$$b_c = p_c/t_c,$$

and the residual sum of squares, with $n-m-1$ degrees of freedom, would be

$$(n-m-1)s^2 = u_c - p_c^2/t_c.$$

The variance of b_c would be estimated from the residual mean square s^2 as

$$s^2/t_c.$$

Similar results (accurate enough for our purpose, despite the possible inequality of sampling of different trees) would apply for the between-trees line of the analysis. Thus the two regression coefficients could be compared and, if it were appropriate, combined.

The sums of squares and products, adjusted to simulate random sampling, are found as follows:

$$u_a = u_o - (\sum_r n_r^2 - n)u_c/n(n-m), \text{ etc.}$$

The second term is small if m is large and may usually be ignored. The divisor is reduced from $n-1$ to $(n - \sum_r n_r^2/n)$ by this adjustment.

Example 8.4   The Regression of Maximum Compressive Strength on Density, for Specimens of Hoop Pine.   Table 8.22 gives the sums of squares and products of maximum compressive strength and density, analyzed into components between and within trees. The total number of specimens taken from the 30 trees is 188, and

$$\sum_r n_r^2 = 1346.$$

The reduced sums of squares and mean squares are given in the final columns of the table.

The regression coefficients and their variances are set out in Table 8.23, in which it is shown that the difference is significant at the 5 per cent level. If the significance of the difference were ignored, the combined regression coefficient would be obtained by weighting the two regression coefficients in the ratio 417.0 : 410.1; its variance, presented in the table, is

$$\frac{410.1 \times 417.0}{410.1 + 417.0}$$

TABLE 8.22

SUMS OF SQUARES AND PRODUCTS OF MAXIMUM COMPRESSIVE STRENGTH (LB./SQ. IN.) (y) AND DENSITY (LB./CU. FT.) (x) FOR SPECIMENS OF HOOP PINE

		Sums of Squares and Products				y, Reduced	
	D.F.	y^2	xy	x^2	D.F.	S.S.	M.S.
Between trees	29	82,857,000	305,790	1,400.3	28	16,080,000	574,300
Within trees	158	47,182,000	78,890	546.8	157	35,800,000	228,000
Total	187	130,039,000	384,680	1,947.1			
Adjusted to random sampling		128,200,000	381,600	1,925.8			

$$\frac{\sum n_r^2 - n}{n(n-m)} = 0.03898$$

TABLE 8.23

REGRESSION COEFFICIENTS FROM DIFFERENT LINES OF TABLE 8.22

	b	Variance	S.E.
Between trees	218.4	410.1	20.3
Within trees	144.3	417.0	20.4
Difference	74.1	827.1	28.8

$t = 74.1/28.8 = 2.57$, significant at 5 per cent level

	b	Variance	S.E.
Combined (weighted)	181.7	206.8	14.4
Total	197.6	245.0	15.7
Adjusted	198.2		

The sums of squares and products, adjusted to random sampling, are given at the foot of Table 8.22, from which the adjusted regression coefficient is derived. Its difference from the total regression coefficient is clearly negligible. The variance of the total regression coefficient may be found by noting that the coefficient is a weighted mean of b_b and b_c, with weights in the ratio 1400.3 : 546.8, or 0.719 : 0.281, so that its variance is

$$410.1 \times 0.719^2 + 417.0 \times 0.281^2 = 245.0.$$

Methods for the combining of information from different sources may be extended to multiple regression. The following example shows how, in a multiple regression, additional information about one of the coefficients may be included. This question is discussed in more detail by Durbin (1953).

Example 8.5   The Effect of Load and Rate of Loading on Time to Failure of Wooden Specimens Loaded in Compression Parallel to the Grain.   An experiment was carried out in which specimens of Queensland maple (*Flindersia brayleyana* F.v.M.) were loaded in compression at various rates of loading, to a predetermined load that was then sustained until the specimen failed.   The object was to study the effects of rate of loading and of sustained load on the time the specimen took to fail.   Since the specimens varied in their intrinsic strength, the loads were standardized as given percentages of the estimated load required for immediate failure; these "ultimate loads" were determined by means of tests on neighboring specimens, with accuracy sufficient for their errors to be ignored in the analysis.

This experiment and its analysis are fully described by Ditchburne (1959).

The specimens were taken from a number of planks; different planks were allocated to different rates of loading, and the specimens of each plank were allocated to different percentage loads.   However, since not every percentage was applied to each plank, the variation between planks, as well as that within planks, contributed some information on the effect of percentage load.

It was found that a satisfactory analysis of the data was given by the regression of $\log_{10}$ (time to failure in seconds) (y) on $\log_{10}$ (percentage load) (x_1) and $\log_{10}$ (rate of loading, in lb./min.) (x_2).   The analysis is therefore carried out as follows.   First, the sums of squares and products of each of the three variables, between and within planks, are calculated; these are shown in Table 8.24.

TABLE 8.24

ANALYSIS OF COVARIANCE OF LOG PERCENTAGE LOAD (x_1), LOG RATE OF LOADING (x_2), AND LOG TIME TO FAILURE (y)

	D.F.	y^2	x_1y	x_2y	x_1^2	x_1x_2	x_2^2
Between planks	49	16.5353	107.350	-26.4452	3191.35	-719.400	167.0640
Within planks	246	162.1796	-629.050	—	3344.64	—	—
Total	295	178.7149	-521.700	-26.4452	6535.99	-719.400	167.0640
$0.7076B + W$		173.8800	-553.089	-18.7126	5602.84	-509.047	118.2145

Then, for each line of the analysis, the reduced sum of squares and mean square of y are calculated, in order to give estimates of the relative precision of between-plank and within-plank comparisons.   These analyses are shown in Table 8.25.   As a by-product, the partial regression coefficients for each line are determined.

In combining the information about b_1 from the between-plank and within-plank variation, some adjustment needs also to be made to the value of b_2, to allow for the change of b_1 from its between-plank estimate, with which the original value of b_2 is associated.   This is done by the following method.   In Table 8.25, the final column shows that the variance between planks exceeds that within planks, the ratio being

$$0.2531/0.1791 = 1.4132.$$

TABLE 8.25

CALCULATION OF REDUCED VARIATION FOR EACH LINE OF TABLE 8.24

| | Regression coefficients | | Sum of Squares | D.F. | Reduced variation | |
	b_1	b_2			Sum of Squares	Mean Square
Between planks	−0.069 790	−0.458 820	4.6416	47	11.8937	0.2531
Within planks	−0.188 077	—	118.3099	245	43.8697	0.1791

Both these variances are estimated from a substantial number of degrees of freedom, so that their errors may be ignored. Hence, in combining the information from variation between planks and within planks, the appropriate weight for the sums of squares and products between planks is

$$1/1.4132 = 0.7076.$$

The values of $0.7076B + W$ (B and W standing for the corresponding sums of squares and products between and within planks respectively) are set out at the foot of Table 8.24. From these combined results the inverse matrix and regression coefficients are determined, in Table 8.26. It is seen that, as might be expected, the final value of b_1 differs little from its within-plank estimate.

TABLE 8.26

COMBINATION OF BETWEEN-PLANK AND WITHIN-PLANK INFORMATION
INVERSE MATRIX (FROM $0.7076B + W$ LINE) AND REGRESSION COEFFICIENTS b_i

$$10^{-6} \times \begin{bmatrix} 293.1848 & 1,262.492 \\ 1,262.492 & 13,895.65 \end{bmatrix} \quad \begin{matrix} -0.185\ 782 \\ -0.958\ 294 \end{matrix}$$

The standard errors of b_1 and b_2 are now determined in the usual way; thus

$$\text{S.E. } (b_1) = \sqrt{(0.1791 \times 293.1848 \times 10^{-6})} = 0.0072$$

$$\text{S.E. } (b_2) = \sqrt{(0.1791 \times 13,895.65 \times 10^{-6})} = 0.050.$$

A comprehensive test may also be made by means of an analysis of variance, as set out in Table 8.27. The sum of squares for regression is found in the usual way, and the total sum of squares is found at the foot of Table 8.24. The residual sum of squares is 292 times the residual mean square within planks from Table 8.25; its actual degrees of freedom are only 245, but formally it is attributed the $47 + 245 = 292$ degrees of freedom for reduced variation from Table 8.25. The sum of squares for difference of regressions is found by subtraction, although it may also be found directly from the comparison of the two regression coefficients b_1 in Table 8.25. The difference of regressions is significant only at the 5 per cent level and may be considered not to invalidate the determination of the combined regression.

TABLE 8.27

ANALYSIS OF VARIANCE (FROM $0.7076B + W$ LINE)

	D.F.	Sum of Squares	Mean Square
Combined regression	2	120.6862	
Difference of regressions	1	0.9083	0.9083*
Residual	292	52.2855	0.1791
Total	295	173.8800	

* Significant at 5 per cent level.

8.9 GENERAL COMMENTS ON HETEROGENEOUS DATA

The last two examples differ from preceding ones in that the different sources of variation are of different *kinds* (between and within trees, between and within planks), whereas in earlier examples the sources of variation were different but of the same kind. The applications of regression analysis to heterogeneous data of the type discussed in the last section are limited, because it is not often realistic to assume that different sources of variation are affecting the variables but that the regression relationships are the same or bear some relation to one another. Furthermore, when the independent variable is subject to random error (as it will often be in data of this type), the regression coefficient is less in absolute value than the corresponding coefficient in the underlying relation (if linear) between the variables. The greater the fraction of the total variation which is random, the greater this effect will be. Thus, in heterogeneous data, the same underlying relation may be reflected in different regression relations. For example, in Example 8.5, the regression coefficient between planks would be expected to exceed that within planks, so that the significant difference noted in the regression coefficients may reflect an even greater difference in the underlying relation. This matter will be considered further in Chapter 11. The object of these remarks is merely to draw attention to the difficulties that can arise with heterogeneous data; it is important, when such data are being treated, to consider carefully the assumptions that are made.

CHAPTER 9

Simultaneous
Regression Equations

9.1 INTRODUCTION

In this chapter we consider the determination and interpretation of simultaneous equations fitted to experimental data. Although little has been written on simultaneous equations in experimentation, their uses in economics have frequently been discussed. In that field, however, there is often no distinction between dependent and independent variables. In what is known in econometrics as a complete system of simultaneous equations, there are as many equations as endogenous variables, so that the equations consist of a linear transformation from the unknown disturbances and known exogenous variables to the observed variables. The treatment of simultaneous equations in econometrics is generally troublesome and depends on the completeness of the system of equations and the identifiability of the parameters.

In experimental work, on the other hand, there is in many situations a clear distinction between the dependent and independent variables. Thus the number of equations will be at most equal to the number of dependent variables. In this field, too, there is a case of particular interest, as will be shown later, which occurs when the numbers of dependent and independent variables are the same. The applications of simultaneous equations to experimental work are quite important and are much more straightforward than those in econometrics, yet, strangely enough, they have been little discussed. The only published work in this field with which we are familiar is that of Box and Hunter (1954), but even this relates to a different situation from that considered here, and to particular applications in experimental design.

We begin by discussing a simple application of simultaneous equations to experimental work. Then will follow the mathematical theory, after which special cases will be discussed.

9.2   A CHEMICAL EXAMPLE

Example 9.1   Simultaneous Estimation of Glucose and Galactose in Solution.   Fisher, Hansen, and Norton (1955) discuss the simultaneous quantitative determination of both glucose and galactose in solutions of unknown chemical composition, by means of optical density measurements. Without going into the technical details, which are given in the paper referred to, we can simply state that solutions of glucose and galactose are treated to develop a color; the optical density of the solution to light of two different wavelengths is then determined, and the two data thus obtained are used to estimate the amount of each sugar in solution. It is assumed that, within the range of concentrations studied, optical density for each sugar is proportional to the amount of sugar; then we make use of the fact that each sugar differs in its density to light of different wavelengths.

Solutions containing known amounts of glucose and galactose were prepared, and the density at two different wavelengths (470 and 560 mμ) was determined. The data enable a regression of density on amount of each sugar to be determined for each wavelength. These regressions then constitute a calibration of the apparatus, such that if optical densities for some unknown solution are substituted in the equations, the amount of each sugar can be estimated.

Thus, if y_1 and y_2 are the optical densities at 470 and 560 mμ respectively, and x_1 and x_2 are the amounts of each sugar (in milligrams), the regression equations may be written

$$Y_1 = b_{11}x_1 + b_{21}x_2$$
$$Y_2 = b_{12}x_1 + b_{22}x_2. \tag{9.1}$$

These equations have no constant term, since the optical densities are zero at zero concentration of the sugars. In the practical use of these equations, the y's will be observed values and the x's predicted. If the equations are solved for this purpose, we get

$$X_1 = b^{11}y_1 + b^{21}y_2$$
$$X_2 = b^{12}y_1 + b^{22}y_2 \tag{9.2}$$

where the matrix

$$\begin{bmatrix} b^{11} & b^{21} \\ b^{12} & b^{22} \end{bmatrix}$$

is the inverse of the original matrix of regression coefficients,

$$\begin{bmatrix} b_{11} & b_{21} \\ b_{12} & b_{22} \end{bmatrix}.$$

The equations (9.2) will be called inverse regression equations, and the X values inverse estimates. It will be seen that in practically every calibration problem inverse estimates are required, since the quantities arbitrarily assigned in the calibration are unknown in the application to estimation.

Problems of this kind are of frequent occurrence in quantitative chemical analysis and in other fields. The determination of the accuracy with which estimates can be made from such equations is an important practical problem. We now give the mathematical derivation of sampling errors and fiducial intervals, before returning to the arithmetical analysis of the example just discussed.

9.3 SIMULTANEOUS EQUATIONS IN GENERAL

In general, we may consider that we have n observations on each of p independent variables x_i $(i = 1, 2, \cdots, p)$ and q dependent variables y_j $(j = 1, 2, \cdots, q)$, and that we must estimate the y_j in terms of the x_i or vice versa. Then we may determine q regression equations

$$Y_j = \sum_i b_{ij} x_i \qquad (j = 1, 2, \cdots; q), \qquad (9.3)$$

in which for simplicity the variables are measured from their means so that the constant terms vanish.

Besides the standard notation used throughout this book, we introduce the following notation:

u_{jk} total sum of products of y_j and y_k $(n - 1$ degrees of freedom)

w_{jk} residual sum of products of y_j and y_k $(n - p - 1$ degrees of freedom)

$U = (u_{jk})$

$W = (w_{jk}) \qquad W^{-1} = (w^{jk})$.

Lower case x_i or y_j will denote either observed or potentially observed (although sometimes actually unknown) quantities, and capital X_i or Y_j will denote estimates based on the observed quantities.

9.4 DIRECT ESTIMATION

If one of the y_j or a linear combination of them is to be estimated from the equations (9.3), the procedure is straightforward. For the estimated variances of the regression coefficients we have the familiar results

$$(n - p - 1) \, V(b_{ij}) = w_{jj} t^{ii}$$

and, generally,

$$(n - p - 1) \, \mathrm{Cov} \, (b_{hj}, b_{ik}) = w_{jk} t^{hi}$$
$$= (n - p - 1) \, \mathrm{Cov} \, (b_{ij}, b_{hk}).$$

Hence, for the variance of an estimate, we have

$$(n - p - 1) \, V(Y_j) = w_{jj} \left(\frac{1}{n} + \sum_h \sum_i t^{hi} x_h x_i \right)$$

and in general for the covariance of any two estimates,

$$(n - p - 1) \operatorname{Cov}(Y_j, Y_k) = w_{jk}\left(\frac{1}{n} + \sum_h \sum_i t^{hi}x_h x_i\right),$$

the term $1/n$ being included to allow for the fact that the variables are measured from their means.

In order to know how much a new observation y_j will vary about the predicted value, we need the variance about an estimate, as well as the variance of the estimate. We have

$$(n - p - 1) V(y_j - Y_j) = Hw_{jj}$$

and, generally,

$$(n - p - 1) \operatorname{Cov}(y_j - Y_j, y_k - Y_k) = Hw_{jk}$$

where

$$H = 1 + \frac{1}{n} + \sum_h \sum_i t^{hi}x_h x_i. \tag{9.4}$$

If it is required to estimate a linear combination of the y_j, for example,

$$y_a = \sum_j a_j y_j,$$

the regression coefficients are linear combinations of the original coefficients, namely,

$$b_{ia} = \sum_j a_j b_{ij},$$

and the regression equation for estimating y_a may be written

$$Y_a = \sum_i b_{ia} x_i.$$

The variance of an estimate is given by

$$(n - p - 1) V(Y_a) = \sum_j \sum_k a_j a_k w_{jk}\left(\frac{1}{n} + \sum_h \sum_i t^{hi}x_h x_i\right).$$

A special case of a linear combination of the dependent variables is Hotelling's "most predictable criterion." For a linear combination with coefficients a_j, the residual sum of squares after fitting the regression on the x_i is

$$\sum_j \sum_k a_j a_k w_{jk} \tag{9.5}$$

and the total sum of squares is

$$\sum_j \sum_k a_j a_k u_{jk}. \tag{9.6}$$

The linear combination which minimizes the ratio of (9.5) to (9.6) will clearly be an estimate of that linear combination least affected by departure from regression; Hotelling has designated it the most predictable criterion. The coefficients a_j will be found as one of the latent vectors of the matrix $W^{-1}U$. Whether this linear combination has any relevance to the interpretation of the data will depend on the nature of the problem.

9.5 INVERSE ESTIMATION

As mentioned earlier, we are most often interested in using a set of simultaneous regression equations inversely for estimating values of the independent variables from observed values of the dependent variables. This situation arises frequently, for example, in calibration experiments, as Example 9.1 shows. Now in order that the regression equations may be solved for the independent variables, it is necessary that the number of equations equal the number of independent variables. If there are fewer equations than independent variables, they cannot be solved, and all that can be determined are certain relationships among the estimated values of the independent variables. On the other hand, if there are more equations than unknown independent variables, we have redundant information; however, by an adaptation of the method of least squares, valid estimates of the unknowns may be determined. Then the discrepancies of the individual equations from these estimates provide a measure of the consistency of the different equations and hence of the different dependent variables. We shall consider each of these cases in turn.

(i) $p = q$

Here the regression equations (9.3) may be solved directly to give the estimates of the x_i, which we denote, without risk of confusion with direct estimates, by X_i. The solutions are

$$X_i = \sum_j b^{ji} y_j,$$

where the b^{ji} are the elements of the matrix inverse to the square matrix

$$B = (b_{ij}).$$

We note that in the matrix B rows correspond to x variables and columns to y variables, whereas in B^{-1} rows correspond to y variables and columns to x variables. Thus, for either direct or inverse regression equations, the regression coefficients corresponding to any predictand are read down the columns.

We shall show below how tolerance limits for values, corresponding to the estimates X_i, may be determined by means of the F test. First of all, however, it is of interest to determine approximate standard errors for these estimates. These standard errors will be applicable when the estimated regression coefficients are large compared with their standard errors, and the inverse regression coefficients are likewise large compared with their standard errors. This second condition requires, in particular, that the matrix B be not almost singular.

Now we have

$$BB^{-1} = I;$$

hence, on taking differentials and multiplying the results by B^{-1}, we find

$$dB^{-1} = -B^{-1}(dB)B^{-1}, \tag{9.7}$$

whence

$$db^{ji} = -\sum_h \sum_k b^{jh} b^{ki}\, db_{hk}. \tag{9.8}$$

The equations (9.7) and (9.8) represent a linear transformation of the differentials db_{hk}. Taking the direct product (van der Waerden, 1931) of such a transformation and its transposed, we have

$$dB^{-1} \times dB'^{-1} = (B^{-1}(dB)B^{-1}) \times (B'^{-1}(dB')B'^{-1})$$
$$= (B^{-1} \times B'^{-1})(dB \times dB')(B^{-1} \times B'^{-1}). \tag{9.9}$$

Now each of the direct products in equation (9.9) is a $p^2 \times p^2$ matrix whose typical elements are products of two regression coefficients or differentials. For instance, the typical element of $dB \times dB'$ is

$$db_{ij}\, db_{i'j'}.$$

If we take expectations of each side of equation (9.9), we obtain on the left-hand side the matrix of variances and covariances of the b^{ji}, whereas on the right-hand side the middle factor gives the matrix of variances and covariances of the b_{ij}. Now, as we have seen, the appropriate estimate of the covariance of b_{ij} and $b_{i'j'}$ is

$$t^{ii'} w_{jj'}/(n - p - 1).$$

If we make a suitable permutation of rows and columns, the expected value of the middle factor therefore becomes the direct product

$$T^{-1} \times W/(n - p - 1),$$

of two $p \times p$ matrices.

After further suitable permutations of rows and columns, we find for the estimated expected value of the left-hand side

$$(B^{-1} \times B'^{-1})(T^{-1} \times W)(B'^{-1} \times B^{-1})/(n - p - 1)$$
$$= (B^{-1}T^{-1}B'^{-1}) \times (B'^{-1}WB^{-1})/(n - p - 1) = M^{-1} \times Q^{-1}/(n - p - 1)$$

where $$M = B'TB$$
and $$Q = BW^{-1}B',$$
so that $$M^{-1} = B^{-1}T^{-1}B'^{-1}$$
and $$Q^{-1} = B'^{-1}WB^{-1}.$$

This result gives in particular

$$(n - p - 1) \operatorname{Cov}(b^{ji}, b^{j'i'}) = m^{jj'}q^{ii'}$$
$$= \sum_h \sum_{h'} t^{hh'} b^{jh} b^{j'h'} \sum_k \sum_{k'} w_{kk'} b^{ki} b^{k'i'}$$
$$= (n - p - 1) \operatorname{Cov}(b^{ji'}, b^{j'i}).$$

These results are, of course, approximate and will often be inaccurate; their interest lies in the fact that the expressions found are similar to those occurring in the exact analysis.

We may now determine approximate variances and covariances of estimates X_i based on observations y_j:

$$(n - p - 1) V(X_i) = (n - p - 1) V(\sum_j b^{ji} y_j)$$

$$= \left(1 + \frac{1}{n}\right) \sum_j \sum_{j'} w_{jj'} b^{ji} b^{j'i} + \sum_j \sum_{j'} \sum_h \sum_{h'} y_j y_{j'} t^{hh'} b^{jh} b^{j'h'} \sum_k \sum_{k'} w_{kk'} b^{ki} b^{k'i}$$

$$= \sum_j \sum_{j'} w_{jj'} b^{ji} b^{j'i} \left(1 + \frac{1}{n} + \sum_h \sum_{h'} t^{hh'} X_h X_{h'}\right). \tag{9.10}$$

This result follows from the formula for the approximate variance of a product, and from the fact that the b^{ji} and the y_j are independent. Similarly, to the same degree of approximation,

$$(n - p - 1) \operatorname{Cov}(X_i, X_{i'}) = \sum_j \sum_{j'} w_{jj'} b^{ji} b^{j'i'} \left(1 + \frac{1}{n} + \sum_h \sum_{h'} t^{hh'} X_h X_{h'}\right).$$

The covariance matrix of the X_i may be written $HQ^{-1}/(n - p - 1)$ where Q^{-1} again equals $B'^{-1}WB^{-1}$, and H is a function of the estimates rather than of observed values as defined in (9.4). It may be noted that these results are analogous to those found in direct estimation of an observation y_j. There we have

$$(n - p - 1) V(y_j - Y_j) = w_{jj}H$$
and
$$(n - p - 1) \operatorname{Cov}(y_j - Y_j, y_{j'} - Y_{j'}) = w_{jj'}H$$

where the x_h are now observed quantities, the Y_j are regression estimates, and the y_j are new observations, not used in determining the regression.

The exact determination of sampling variation is not much more complicated. We may find simultaneous fiducial limits for the unknown quantities x_i in the following way. The ratio

$$\frac{n-2p}{p} \frac{\sum_j \sum_k w^{jk}(y_j - \sum_i b_{ij}x_i)(y_k - \sum_i b_{ik}x_i)}{H}$$

is distributed as F with p and $n-2p$ degrees of freedom. By substituting various sets of values of the x_i in the formula, we can determine for which sets the associated value of F is nonsignificant, and hence which sets are concordant with the data. The range of concordant sets of the x_i defines a fiducial region for the values.

Now, since we may write

$$y_j = \sum_i b_{ij}X_i,$$

the y_j being observations and the X_i estimates, we have

$$\sum_j \sum_k w^{jk}(y_j - \sum_i b_{ij}x_i)(y_k - \sum_i b_{ik}x_i) = \sum_h \sum_i \sum_j \sum_k (X_h - x_h)(X_i - x_i)w^{jk}b_{hj}b_{ik}$$

$$= \sum_h \sum_i (X_h - x_h)(X_i - x_i)q_{hi} \quad (9.11)$$

where

$$q_{hi} = \sum_j \sum_k w^{jk}b_{hj}b_{ik}.$$

Since q_{hi} is a typical element of the matrix

$$Q = BW^{-1}B',$$

expression (9.11) may be written

$$(X - x)BW^{-1}B'(X' - x').$$

Hence the simultaneous fiducial limits for the values x_i are given by the solution (if real) of

$$F = \frac{n-2p}{p} \frac{\sum_h \sum_i (X_h - x_h)(X_i - x_i)q_{hi}}{H}.$$

If limits for a single value x_h are required, we have

$$V(X_h) = Hq^{hh}/(n - p - 1). \quad (9.12)$$

Now since

$$Q = BW^{-1}B',$$
$$Q^{-1} = B'^{-1}WB^{-1},$$

so that

$$q^{hi} = \sum_j \sum_k w_{jk}b^{jh}b^{ki}.$$

Hence, with 1 and $n - p - 1$ degrees of freedom,

$$F = \frac{(n - p - 1)(X_h - x_h)^2}{H \sum_j \sum_k w_{jk} b^{jh} b^{kh}}.$$

Note that the variance estimate given by (9.12) differs from the approximate estimate given in (9.10) by the replacement of calculated quantities X_i by unknowns x_i. In practice, since the x_i are unknown, the approximate variance estimate based on the X_i would need to be used to give fiducial limits for a single x_h.

(ii) $p < q$

We have now more equations than unknowns. We have a choice either of omitting $q - p$ of the equations (provided we can decide from prior considerations which are least useful), or of using the additional information given by the equations to test the consistency of the relationships involving the different dependent variables. This latter aspect is the one that we shall examine.

If an observation of a set y_j ($j = 1, 2, \cdots, q$) of dependent variables is to be used to estimate a set x_i ($i = 1, 2, \cdots, p$), we may so determine the estimate that it has minimum (estimated) variance. Now since the estimated covariance of y_j and y_k is proportional to w_{jk}, the quantity to be minimized, with respect to the x_i, is

$$\sum_j \sum_k w^{jk} (y_j - \sum_i b_{ij} x_i)(y_k - \sum_i b_{ik} x_i).$$

If we put, as in (i),

$$Q = BW^{-1}B',$$

so that

$$q_{hi} = \sum_j \sum_k w^{jk} b_{hj} b_{ik},$$

and also put

$$P = BW^{-1}\mathbf{y},$$

so that

$$p_i = \sum_j \sum_k w^{jk} b_{ij} y_k,$$

we find for the normal equations

$$QX = P,$$

that is,

$$\sum_h q_{hi} X_h = p_i,$$

so that

$$\mathbf{X} = Q^{-1}P$$

or

$$X_h = \sum_i q^{hi} p_i.$$

These results are similar to those found for the case $p = q$, except that here the matrix B does not possess an inverse, so that the estimates need to be expressed in terms of the matrices P and Q.

As in the case $p = q$, the estimated covariance matrix of the X_i is

$$\frac{H}{n - p - 1} Q^{-1}.$$

Now we may test the consistency of the q equations by means of the departures of the observed y_j values from the estimates provided by inserting the X_i in the equations. The criterion is

$$\frac{(n - p - q)}{q - p} \frac{\sum_j \sum_k w^{jk}(y_j - \sum_i b_{ij}X_i)(y_k - \sum_i b_{ik}X_i)}{H},$$

which is distributed as F with $q - p$ and $n - p - q$ degrees of freedom. This may be written in the alternative forms:

$$\frac{n - p - q}{(q - p)H} \left(\sum_j \sum_k w^{jk}y_jy_k - \sum_h \sum_i q_{hi}X_hX_i\right)$$

or

$$\frac{n - p - q}{(q - p)H} \left(\sum_j \sum_k w^{jk}y_jy_k - \sum_h \sum_i q^{hi}p_hp_i\right).$$

If the value of F is not significant, there is no evidence for regarding the equations as inconsistent, and fiducial limits may be determined for the x_i. For these we have

$$F = \frac{(n - p - q)}{pH} \sum_h \sum_i q_{hi}(X_h - x_h)(X_i - x_i)$$

with p and $n - p - q$ degrees of freedom. This may be written in the alternative form

$$F = \frac{n - p - q}{pH} \sum_h \sum_{h'} q^{hh'}(p_h - \sum_i x_iq_{hi})(p_{h'} - \sum_i x_iq_{h'i}).$$

By means of this criterion, the concordance of any set of x_i with the data may be established.

In the particular case when $p = 1$, the solution of the equations gives the discriminant function for assigning a value of x_1 on the basis of observations of the q variables $y_1, y_2, \cdots, y_q$.

The discriminant function is

$$X_1 = p_1/q_{11}$$

$$= \frac{\sum_j \sum_k w^{jk}b_{1j}y_k}{\sum_j \sum_k w^{jk}b_{1j}b_{1k}}.$$

To test the consistency of any set of observations y_j, the criterion is

$$\frac{n-q-1}{q-1} \frac{\sum_j \sum_k w^{jk} y_j y_k - p_1{}^2/q_{11}}{\left(1 + \dfrac{1}{n} + \dfrac{x_1{}^2}{t_{11}}\right)}$$

with $q-1$ and $n-q-1$ degrees of freedom.

It should be remarked here that this is a test not of the discriminant function, which has been established from previous data, but of the consistency of the present set of observations. A significant result may indicate either that the values of y_j are not consistent among themselves, or that the discriminant function determined from previous data does not apply to the present observations.

(iii) $p > q$

Here we have fewer equations than unknowns, so that estimates of the unknown x_i cannot be determined. The most that can be done is to find a relationship among $p - q + 1$ of the estimates X_i. In many cases such a relationship may be all that is required. An example of such a relationship has already been given in Example 6.2.

Suppose that we wish to eliminate $X_1, X_2, \cdots, X_{q-1}$ and to determine the relationship among $X_q, X_{q+1}, \cdots, X_p$. The determinant of the first $q - 1$ rows of B and the $q - 1$ columns resulting from omitting column j will be denoted by $(-1)^{j-1}B_j$. Then it is readily shown that the required relationship is

$$\sum_{j=1}^{q} B_j \sum_{i=q}^{p} b_{ij} X_i = \sum_{j=1}^{q} B_j y_j.$$

The fiducial limits for the corresponding relationship among the x_i can be determined only approximately.

The fact that p exceeds q does not, however, prevent simultaneous fiducial limits for the x_i from being found. The criterion, distributed as F with q and $n - p - q$ degrees of freedom, from which simultaneous fiducial limits may be derived, is

$$\frac{n-p-q}{qH} \sum_j \sum_k w^{jk}(y_j - \sum_i b_{ij}x_i)(y_k - \sum_i b_{ik}x_i)$$

$$= \frac{n-p-q}{qH} \sum_h \sum_i q_{hi}(X_h - x_h)(X_i - x_i)$$

where q_{hi} is the typical element of the matrix Q defined in (i) and (ii). Here Q, although it is a $p \times p$ matrix, is of rank q.

9.6 DISCUSSION OF THE CHEMICAL EXAMPLE

Example 9.1 (Continued from Section 9.2). The original data of the experiment discussed in Section 9.2 are given by Fisher, Hansen, and Norton (1955) in their Table I and are not reproduced here.

Fisher et al. fitted quadratic regression equations to their data, but since we found that the quadratic terms were significant only at the 5 per cent level for optical densities at 560 mμ (y_2), we have ignored these terms and fitted only linear regressions. The analyses of variance and covariance of y_1 and y_2 are shown in Table 9.1, and the B, T, and W matrices and their inverses in Table 9.2.

TABLE 9.1

ANALYSES OF VARIANCE AND COVARIANCE OF OPTICAL DENSITY
MEASUREMENTS AT 470 mμ (y_1) AND AT 560 mμ (y_2) (FISHER,
HANSEN, AND NORTON'S DATA)

	D.F.	Sums of Squares and Products		
		y_1^2	$y_1 y_2$	y_2^2
Regression on x_1, x_2	2	2.570 253	4.207 267	6.995 805
Residual	26	0.003 167	0.002 996	0.006 733
Total	28	2.573 420	4.210 263	7.002 538

TABLE 9.2

MATRICES OF SUMS OF SQUARES AND PRODUCTS AND OF REGRESSION
COEFFICIENTS

$$T = \begin{bmatrix} 0.2500 & 0.0750 \\ 0.0750 & 0.2500 \end{bmatrix} \qquad 10^6 W = \begin{bmatrix} 3167 & 2996 \\ 2996 & 6733 \end{bmatrix} \qquad B = \begin{bmatrix} 1.2166 & 1.3465 \\ 2.6240 & 4.7276 \end{bmatrix}$$

$$T^{-1} = \begin{bmatrix} 4.3956 & -1.3187 \\ -1.3187 & 4.3956 \end{bmatrix} \qquad W^{-1} = \begin{bmatrix} 545.3 & -242.6 \\ -242.6 & 256.5 \end{bmatrix} \qquad B^{-1} = \begin{bmatrix} 2.1311 & -0.6070 \\ -1.1829 & 0.5484 \end{bmatrix}$$

Thus we see from Table 9.2 that the direct regression equations are

$$Y_1 = 1.2166x_1 + 2.6240x_2$$
$$Y_2 = 1.3465x_1 + 4.7276x_2$$

and the inverse equations are

$$X_1 = 2.1311y_1 - 1.1829y_2$$
$$X_2 = -0.6070y_1 + 0.5484y_2$$

in agreement with the results of Fisher et al.

The direct equations are less useful than the inverse ones. Since, in this example, the numbers of dependent and independent variables are equal, no test for consistency is possible, but we can derive fiducial limits for the values of x_1 and x_2 corresponding to observed values y_1 and y_2.

Since the inverse regression coefficients, as well as the direct coefficients, are likely to be well determined, we may calculate their approximate standard errors. Table 9.3 gives the matrices $B^{-1}T^{-1}B'^{-1}$ and $B'^{-1}WB^{-1}$ required in

TABLE 9.3

MATRIX PRODUCTS REQUIRED IN ESTIMATING VARIANCES

$$M^{-1} = B^{-1}T^{-1}B'^{-1} \qquad 10^6(Q^{-1} = B'^{-1}WB^{-1})$$

$$\begin{bmatrix} 24.995 & -15.032 \\ -15.032 & 9.183 \end{bmatrix} \qquad \begin{bmatrix} 8699 & -2812 \\ -2812 & 1197 \end{bmatrix}$$

these calculations. Then, for example, the variance of b^{21} is obtained using the second diagonal term of $B^{-1}T^{-1}B'^{-1}$ and the first diagonal term of $B'^{-1}WB^{-1}$:

$$9.183 \times 10^{-6} \times 8699/26 = 0.003\,072,$$

so that the standard error of b^{21} is 0.055. The standard errors of the coefficients may be set out as follows:

$$\begin{bmatrix} 0.091 & 0.034 \\ 0.055 & 0.021 \end{bmatrix}.$$

For general purposes, of course, the covariances as well as the variances will be of interest.

In determining the approximate variance of an estimate X_i, since the regression is through the origin rather than the point of means, the actual values of the y_j rather than departures from means are used, and the term $1/n$ is omitted from the variance estimates, in equation (9.10).

Thus, approximately,

$$V(X_1) = \frac{10^{-6} \times 8699}{26}(1 + 24.99y_1{}^2 - 30.06y_1y_2 + 9.18y_2{}^2)$$

$$= \frac{10^{-6} \times 8699}{26}(1 + 4.396X_1{}^2 - 2.637X_1X_2 + 4.396X_2{}^2)$$

with similar results for Cov (X_1, X_2) and $V(X_2)$.

CHAPTER 10

Discriminant Functions

10.1 INTRODUCTION

The individuals forming a sample can often be classified into two or more groups.   It is then of interest to determine which of the characteristics of these individuals enable the distinctions between groups to be most clearly made.   If several such characteristics can be measured on each of the individuals, it may be found that some linear function of these variables is more efficacious in distinguishing the groups than is any one of them. Thus, for example, certain counts on fish are known as meristic counts; the sum of these counts for any individual is called the meristic index and is used as the basis for distinguishing different races of fish.   Likewise, in anthropometry, various skull measurements have in the past been combined to give what has been called a "coefficient of racial likeness."

Any method of combining different variables is to some extent arbitrary, so that the choice of the linear combination is usually based on some criterion considered to be appropriate.   The most satisfactory feature of the indexes mentioned is their simplicity, although they have probably little else to recommend them.   Sometimes the manner of combining variables will be dictated by the conditions of the problem.   Thus, if wheat and straw yields resulting from different treatments have been determined, the total value of the crop for each treatment is likely to be of interest; then each yield may be weighted by its current price.

When the purpose of the analysis is to determine a linear function of the variables that distinguishes most clearly among the several groups, the linear function is known as a discriminant function.   It is estimated from the data as that function for which the ratio of the sum of squares between groups to the residual sum of squares is a maximum.   The idea of using a discriminant function was first applied by Barnard (1935) to measurements of Egyptian skulls, of known dynastic period, the object being to classify other skulls, of unknown age, with minimum chance of error.   It has since been applied in many other investigations in which multiple measurements can be made.

In the present chapter, the uses of discriminant functions, and the methods of determining them, will be outlined. Tests for the adequacy of an assigned discriminant function (i.e., for some given system of weighting the variables) to account for the relation existing between the variables and the group effects will be given. The theory of discriminant analysis that is relevant to practical needs is an extension of multiple regression, and most of the required significance tests can be carried out by means of the analysis of variance. Thus, as will be shown later, although the general theory of multivariate analysis is very complicated mathematically, the theory required for significance tests and estimation is not beyond the scope of this book.

10.2 RELATIONSHIP OF DISCRIMINANT FUNCTION FOR A SINGLE COMPARISON WITH MULTIPLE REGRESSION

Multiple regression relations may be validly determined by the methods described in earlier chapters, provided the values of the independent variable y are normally distributed about the regression function; there is then no restriction on the distribution of the x_i, which may even be formally defined variables, representing differences between groups within the population. It can be shown that the theory likewise applies when y is only a formally defined variable (representing a difference between groups or treatments, for example), provided the x values then have normal distributions, with the same covariance matrix, within each group. A formal multiple regression of y on the x_i can be calculated and the standard errors of the coefficients determined in the usual way. The linear combination of the x_i which makes up the regression function is known in this case as a discriminant function, since it serves to discriminate between the groups that the values of y represent, and in fact maximizes the ratio of the between-groups (i.e., regression) sum of squares to the total sum of squares.

When there are more than two groups to be distinguished, the analysis as a formal multiple regression can still be applied, provided only one of the comparisons between groups is relevant. For example, Barnard (1935) considered the linear regression of each of the variables on time as the only relevant comparison. In the same way, Day and Sandomire (1942), in predicting the age of white tail deer, determined a discriminant function for the linear regression of various characters on a measure of age. In many practical problems the conditions of the experiment will define a single comparison which is relevant.

10.3 SCALE CONVENTION

As just described, the determination of a discriminant function in no way differs from that of a multiple regression function.   The scale of the discriminant function is, however, arbitrary, since the values given to y to represent the two groups are arbitrary; in other words, the discriminant ratio is unaffected if all the coefficients in the linear function are increased in the same proportion.

It is convenient, both for the mathematical analysis and for numerical computations, so to choose the scale of the discriminant function that the total sum of squares (or, in general, the sum of the between-groups and residual sums of squares) shall be unity.   The advantage of this convention is that, when additional variables are included in the discriminant function, the reduction in the residual sum of squares correctly reflects the improvement in discrimination attributable to the new variables and can immediately be tested for significance.

This convention is mentioned here because some workers adopt the convention of keeping the residual sum of squares constant.   It should be noted that any such convention is arbitrary and is adopted only for convenience.

10.4 CALCULATION OF DISCRIMINANT FUNCTION
FOR TWO GROUPS (OR ANY SINGLE COMPARISON)

When the comparison of interest is the difference of two groups, the difference of group means for each of the x_i (denoted by d_i) is proportional to the formal sum of products of y and x_i; thus in the usual normal equations of multiple regression the p_i may be replaced by d_i. If the sizes of sample from the two groups are n_1 and n_2, the coefficient of proportionality, to make the total sum of squares of y unity, is k, where

$$k^2 = \frac{n_1 n_2}{n_1 + n_2}.$$

We accordingly have, with the usual notation, t_{hi} denoting the total sum of products of x_h and x_i,

$$\sum_h b_h t_{hi} = k d_i$$

$$b_h = k \sum_i t^{hi} d_i.$$

Then the discriminant function is

$$Y = \sum_i b_i x_i.$$

The analysis of variance of y is set out in Table 10.1 where $n = n_1 + n_2 - 1$.

TABLE 10.1

	D.F.	Sum of Squares
Regression on $x_1, x_2, \cdots, x_p$	p	$k \sum_i b_i d_i = \sum_h \sum_i b_h b_i t_{hi}$
Residual	$n - p$	$1 - k \sum_i b_i d_i$
Total	n	1

An equivalent result is given by the analysis of variance of Y between and within groups, as in Table 10.2.

TABLE 10.2

	D.F.	Sum of Squares
Between groups	p	$k^2(\sum_i b_i d_i)^2$
Within groups	$n - p$	$k \sum_i b_i d_i(1 - k \sum_i b_i d_i)$
Total	n	$\sum_h \sum_i b_h b_i t_{hi} = k \sum_i b_i d_t$

There are several questions that can be answered from this analysis (apart from the over-all significance of discrimination, which is given by the analysis directly). We may first of all be interested in the significance of one coefficient or a set of them, indicating whether the corresponding variables contribute significantly to the discrimination. The sum of squares for the coefficient b_h is simply

$$b_h^2/t^{hh},$$

which may be tested in the usual way against the mean square from the first analysis. For computing purposes this sum of squares may be more conveniently written as

$$k^2(\sum_i t^{hi}d_i)^2/t^{hh}.$$

Alternatively, the variance of b_h is found by multiplying the residual mean square by t^{hh}.

Another aspect that will almost certainly need to be tested is the significance of departure of the coefficients from any assigned set of coefficients β_i (this is a generalization of the over-all test given by the analysis of variance). In particular, by putting some of the β_i zero, we can test the significance of the corresponding variables. Since the scale of the given coefficients may be arbitrary, it needs to be adjusted to make the given coefficients comparable with the estimated ones. It can be shown that the scale convention is such that

$$\sum_h \sum_i \beta_h \beta_i t_{hi} = k \sum_i \beta_i d_i.$$

With this convention, the sum of squares between groups for the hypothetical discriminator

$$\eta = \sum_i \beta_i x_i$$

is

$$k \sum_i \beta_i d_i$$

with one degree of freedom. The sum of squares for departure from the hypothetical discriminator is then

$$k \sum_i (b_i - \beta_i) d_i$$

with $p - 1$ degrees of freedom. We thus have the analysis in Table 10.3.

TABLE 10.3

	D.F.	Sum of Squares
Hypothetical discriminator	1	$k \sum_i \beta_i d_i$
Departure from hypothetical discriminator	$p - 1$	$k \sum_i (b_i - \beta_i) d_i$
Residual	$n - p$	$1 - k \sum_i b_i d_i$
Total	n	1

Example 10.1 Effect of Milking Treatment on Lactation Rate of Merino Ewes. To test the effect of a milking treatment on the lactation rate of ewes, twelve ewes were chosen and allotted at random to three groups of four. At any stage of the experiment those of one group were left untreated (treatment O), those of another had the treatment applied to the left half of the udder (treatment L), and the remaining group had the treatment applied to the right half (treatment R). The treatments were applied at three different stages of lactation, two weeks, six weeks, and twelve weeks, the arrangement forming

four Latin squares, so that each ewe received each treatment at one or another stage of lactation. The treatment layout is shown in Table 10.4, together with lactation rates (ml./hr.) determined for each half and denoted by *l* and *r*.

TABLE 10.4

LACTATION RATES (ml./hr.) OF EWES UNDER DIFFERENT TREATMENTS

Sheep	Stage of Lactation					
No.	2 weeks		6 weeks		12 weeks	
1	*L*		*R*		*O*	
	40.3	23.2	17.4	15.0	7.4	6.8
2	*O*		*L*		*R*	
	26.6	26.6	16.9	14.0	6.1	5.8
3	*R*		*O*		*L*	
	29.5	26.7	16.2	14.6	9.9	8.1
4	*L*		*R*		*O*	
	19.9	14.2	16.1	11.6	11.0	7.0
5	*O*		*L*		*R*	
	18.4	23.4	8.3	14.3	2.3	11.2
6	*R*		*O*		*L*	
	23.1	26.3	13.3	13.4	8.7	7.8
7	*R*		*L*		*O*	
	21.8	29.5	13.6	13.8	9.8	9.4
8	*O*		*R*		*L*	
	24.2	20.3	16.5	14.3	8.5	6.9
9	*L*		*O*		*R*	
	17.3	15.7	13.8	18.8	5.1	8.1
10	*R*		*L*		*O*	
	17.7	17.7	14.3	12.1	8.4	8.3
11	*O*		*R*		*L*	
	19.4	17.8	11.7	11.3	5.7	6.1
12	*L*		*O*		*R*	
	42.3	37.5	18.1	19.3	11.4	11.8

L = treatment applied to left half
R = treatment applied to right half
O = no treatment applied
The left and right figures are lactation rates for left and right halves respectively.

In the analysis, the treatment effects are separated into two orthogonal comparisons:

    (i) average difference between treated and control, $\frac{1}{2}(L + R) - O$, and
    (ii) difference between treatment of left half and treatment of right half, $L - R$.

The analysis of variance and covariance of the two measurements is shown in Table 10.5. For simplicity, only as much of the analysis as is required for the present example is given here. It is to be expected that the effect (i) will be the same for both halves, and that it can be efficiently estimated from the sum $l + r$; on the other hand, the effect (ii) for one half will be opposite to that for the other half and may be estimated from the difference $l - r$. The analyses of the quantities $l + r$ and $l - r$ are therefore also shown in Table 10.5.

The analysis shows that effect (i), namely the average difference between treatments and control, is negligible; this would imply that, if any effect of treatment exists, it is to divert milk from one half to the other without altering its total amount. This is confirmed by the analysis of $l - r$, which shows that treatment of the left half increases the rate of lactation for the left half at the expense of the right, and vice versa. The averages are

Treated half	32.92 ml./hr.
Untreated half	29.37 ml./hr.
Difference	3.55 ml./hr.

These results complete the main part of the analysis of the data. It is, however, of some interest to test whether there is any asymmetry between the halves, which would be indicated by some combination other than $l - r$ showing up more significantly the effect $L - R$. The relevant test is that of the hypothetical discriminator $l - r$.

From the sums of squares in Table 10.5 and the differences shown at the foot we may write down the normal equations for the coefficients of l and r as follows:

$$406.16b_l + 212.20b_r = 2.25k$$
$$212.20b_l + 267.43b_r = -1.30k$$

where $k = \sqrt{6}$ since $n_l = n_r = 12$.

The solutions are

$$b_l = 0.013\ 800\ 4k$$
$$b_r = -0.015\ 811\ 4k,$$

TABLE 10.5

SUMS OF SQUARES AND PRODUCTS OF RESULTS FOR LEFT AND RIGHT
HALVES; AND SUMS OF SQUARES FOR TOTAL AND DIFFERENCE

	D.F.	l^2	lr	r^2	$l + r$	$l - r$
Sheep	11	539.74	232.20	321.07	1325.21	396.41
Stages	2	1796.57	1578.62	1387.63	6341.44	26.96
Treatments $L + R - 2(O)$	1	1.74	−1.31	0.98	0.10	5.34
$L - R$	1	30.38	−17.55	10.14	5.42	75.62**
Residual	20	375.78	229.75	257.29	1092.57	173.57
Residual + $(L - R)$	21	406.16	212.20	267.43	—	249.19
Total	35	2744.21	2021.71	1977.11	8764.74	677.90
Residual mean square					54.63	8.678
Total of results $L - R$		27.0		−15.6	11.4	42.6
Mean of results $L - R$		2.25		−1.30		

** Significant at 1 per cent level

so that the sum of squares for the treatment effect (ii) is

$$6(0.013\ 800\ 4 \times 2.25 + 0.015\ 811\ 4 \times 1.30) = 0.3096.$$

Now for the hypothetical discriminator the corresponding treatment sum of squares is

$$75.62/249.19 = 0.3035,$$

so that the analysis of variance is as shown in Table 10.6. It is seen that, as

TABLE 10.6
ANALYSIS TO TEST THE DISCRIMINANT FUNCTION

	D.F.	Sum of Squares	Mean Square
$L - R$, Based on $l - r$	1	0.3035	
Additional due to discriminant function	1	0.0061	$0.0061^{(n)}$
	2	0.3096	
Residual	19	0.6904	0.03634
Residual $+ (L - R)$	21	1.0000	

[n] Not significant

might be expected, the adjustment of the ratio $b_l : b_r$ from the theoretical value -1 to the value derived from the data has not had any significant effect on the discriminant ratio. The calculations show how the existence of any asymmetry may be tested and its magnitude assessed.

10.5 DISCRIMINANT FUNCTION FOR A REGRESSION RELATIONSHIP

Before considering the general case of discriminant analysis when there are more than two comparisons of interest among the groups to be compared, we now consider the case in which the comparison of interest is the regression of the variable on some known variable. For example, Finney (1952), describing possible applications of multiple measurements to biological assay, points out that the linear regression of each measurement on the dosage is the relevant comparison, and that a combination of several measurements should be used only as it materially increases the precision of this regression. Again, in Barnard's (1935) investigation of Egyptian skulls, the variation of different characters with time was being studied, the object being to date subsequently found skulls of unknown origin. Hence, the group comparison considered was the regression of each character on time. The discriminant function chosen was that combination of characters most highly correlated with time; and, since the variation between groups was represented by a single comparison, the discriminant function could be determined by the general methods given in Section 10.4. The discriminant function in this case is actually equivalent to the multiple regression function of time on the skull measurements.

Further analyses of these data have already been made by Bartlett (1947) and Rao (1952). The analysis which follows differs somewhat from each of these, although we have used some of Rao's results.

Example 10.2 Discriminant Function for Determining Age of Skulls. In Table 10.7 are shown, for four series of Egyptian skulls, the

TABLE 10.7
MEANS OF FOUR CHARACTERS IN FOUR SERIES OF SKULLS
(From Rao, Table 7*d*. 5α)

Series	N	x_1	x_2	x_3	x_4
I	91	133.582 418	98.307 692	50.835 165	133.000 000
II	162	134.265 432	96.462 963	51.148 148	134.882 716
III	70	134.731 429	96.857 143	50.100 000	133.642 857
IV	75	135.306 667	95.040 000	52.093 333	131.466 667

means of the following four measurements: basialveolar height (x_1), nasal height (x_2), maximum breadth (x_3), and basibregmatic height (x_4). Table 10.8

TABLE 10.8
TOTAL SUMS OF SQUARES AND PRODUCTS OF THE SKULL
MEASUREMENTS AND THE TIME VARIABLE
(397 degrees of freedom)
(cf. Rao, Table 7*d*. 5β)

x_1	x_2	x_3	x_4	t
9785.18	214.20	1217.93	2019.82	718.76
214.20	9559.46	1131.72	2381.13	−1407.26
1217.93	1131.72	4088.73	1133.47	410.10
2019.82	2381.13	1133.47	9382.24	−733.43
				4307.67

shows the over-all sums of squares and products of the four variables. Since the time intervals between the four series are assumed to be in the ratios 2 : 1 : 2, the time variate is given the values −5, −1, 1, 5 for the four series. The sum of products of each measurement with time as thus defined and the sum of squares of time are also shown in Table 10.8. From these the multiple regression of time on the measurements is determined. Table 10.9 gives the inverse matrix and the partial regression (or discriminant) coefficients, and Table 10.10

TABLE 10.9

INVERSE MATRIX FOR THE x VARIABLES; REGRESSION COEFFICIENTS
AND STANDARD ERRORS

					b	S.E
$10^{-6} \times$	110.119	6.355	−28.496	−21.877	0.074 565	± 0.0332
	6.355	114.329	−25.985	−27.244	−0.146 998	± 0.0338
	−28.496	−25.985	265.622	−19.360	0.139 217	± 0.0516
	−21.877	−27.244	−19.360	120.547	−0.073 737	± 0.0347

TABLE 10.10

ANALYSIS OF VARIANCE OF THE TIME VARIATE t

	D.F.	Sum of Squares	Mean Square
Regression	4	371.63	
Residual	393	3936.04	10.02
Total	397	4307.67	

gives the analysis of variance, from whose error mean square the standard errors of the coefficients are calculated. Although this analysis is formal only, in that the appropriate regression is that of the measurements on time, it nevertheless provides valid standard errors and significance tests, as explained earlier.

The analysis shows that all the variables contribute significantly to the regression, the contributions of x_1 and x_4 being significant at the 5 per cent level, the other two at the 1 per cent level. If the regression of the population discriminator on time is assumed to be linear, simultaneous fiducial limits for the coefficients β_1, β_2, β_3, and β_4 may be determined as the sets of values that make significant the sum of squares for departure of the regression coefficients from their theoretical values, as described in Chapter 3.

10.6 TEST OF AN ASSIGNED DISCRIMINANT FUNCTION

In the previous section we have considered the analysis in which, although there are more than two groups, the discriminant function is determined with respect to one specified comparison between groups. We now consider the converse of this, where the discriminator is a specified linear combination of the independent variables. The analysis of variance of such a discriminator provides the needed test for the significance of the group differences which it is supposed to reveal, and it can be seen that such an analysis is of the same form as the analysis in which a group comparison is specified.   We may, however, take the analysis further and test also the adequacy of the specified discriminator, taking into account the variation between groups of the original independent variables.   A corresponding analysis would have been possible with the example given in the last section, wherein we could have tested the linearity of the regression of time on the measurement variables, or, in other words, the adequacy of time to represent the variation between groups.   This analysis will in fact be made in the next section, but since there are more than two comparisons between groups, the analysis is a little more complicated than that in which there are only two comparisons (or correspondingly, two independent variables).   We here consider the test for the adequacy of a discriminator based on two independent variables. In such a case, the effect of the given discriminator may be eliminated by covariance, and the adjusted analysis provides the test of its adequacy.

In the general case with more than two groups, when there are two or more group comparisons, the analysis of the data and the tests that are required are more complicated.   The linear function that best discriminates one comparison is not generally best for another comparison; in other words, a single discriminator is not usually adequate to specify all the differences among the groups.   Such a specification is adequate only when the different groups or populations are collinear, which means that the changes in the mean values for the different variables from one population to another are proportional.

Thus it will be seen that, with more than two groups, the test for the adequacy of a given discriminator has two aspects: the test for the assigned coefficients, which is similar to the test given when there are two groups, and may be called the test for direction, and the even more crucial test for the collinearity of the groups, which is actually a test of whether any single discriminator is adequate to specify group differences.   If the test shows significant departure in direction, a discriminant function with different coefficients may still be tried; but if the test shows significant departure of the data from collinearity, no single discriminant function can adequately specify the differences among the populations.   In practice, of course, even if the groups are not collinear, it may still be convenient to use a single linear function if it discriminates satisfactorily.

Example 10.3 Discrimination between Hybrid Strains of Euca-lyptus. Between two widely separated stands of Eucalyptus trees, one considered to be *E. maculosa* and the other *E. elaeophora*, was a region containing trees believed to be hybrids of these two species.   The presumed hybrid trees were classified on the basis of botanical characteristics into groups believed to be of approximately the same genetical composition. Specimens of wood were taken from a number of trees, both of the parental types and the hybrids, and determinations of density and maximum compressive strength were made on each. The purpose of the investigation was to determine whether either density or maximum compressive strength, or some combination of them, satisfactorily discriminated the different botanical types.

The relevant data from this investigation are set out in Table 10.11. In this

TABLE 10.11

MEAN DENSITY AND MAXIMUM COMPRESSIVE STRENGTH FOR PARENTAL AND HYBRID GROUPS, OF *E. maculosa* AND *E. elaeophora*

Botanical Classification, percentage *E. maculosa*	Number of Trees	Density, x_1	Maximum Compressive Strength, x_2
0	10	43.61	5500
10–30	3	45.33	5550
40–60	3	39.67	4670
70–90	5	40.58	4910
100	10	37.01	4569
Total	31	40.78	5029

example there are five groups (the parental types and three presumed hybrid groups). As the botanical classification is not definite enough to provide a variable with which to correlate the properties of the wood, the dispersion is analyzed between and within groups. The sums of squares and products of density (x_1) and maximum compressive strength (x_2) are shown in Table 10.12.

TABLE 10.12

SUMS OF SQUARES AND PRODUCTS OF DENSITY x_1 AND MAXIMUM COMPRESSIVE STRENGTH x_2

	D.F.	x_1^2	$x_1 x_2$	x_2^2
Between classes	4	288.33	39,106	5,606,200
Within classes	26	191.06	25,731	7,126,100
Total	30	479.39	64,837	12,732,300
Fraction of sum of squares between classes		0.60		0.44

It is seen that, whereas 60 per cent of the variation in density is between groups, there is only 44 per cent between groups for compressive strength. Taking density as the specified discriminator, we need to test whether compressive strength adds anything to the discrimination. The test is carried out by means of an analysis of covariance as described in Chapter 7. After adjustment for density, the variation of compressive strength between groups is tested. The adjusted sum of squares between groups breaks up into two parts, the reduced sum of squares and a sum of squares for difference of regressions within groups and between groups. The reduced sum of squares gives evidence whether a single discriminator is adequate for specifying differences among the groups; the "difference of regressions" term indicates whether the chosen discriminator could be significantly improved and hence provides the test of direction of the discriminator. The analysis, which is set out in Table 10.13, shows that density is a satisfactory discriminator for these data.

TABLE 10.13

ANALYSIS OF VARIANCE OF MAXIMUM COMPRESSIVE STRENGTH x_2, ADJUSTED FOR DENSITY x_1

	D.F.	Sum of Squares	Mean Square
Difference of regressions (Direction)	1	100	100[n]
Between classes, reduced (Collinearity)	3	302,300	100,800[n]
Within classes, reduced	25	3,660,800	146,400
Total, reduced	29	3,963,200	

[n] Not significant

10.7 COMPREHENSIVE ANALYSIS WITH MORE THAN TWO VARIABLES AND MORE THAN TWO COMPARISONS BETWEEN GROUPS

In general, when p and q (the numbers of x and y variables (or group comparisons) respectively) both exceed two, the analysis required is a generalization of the analysis of covariance. We need still to test two aspects of the data—the collinearity of the groups and the adequacy of the specified discriminator—but, since there are more than two variables in either set, the elimination of the discriminator by covariance leaves more than one adjusted variable. The test for collinearity has therefore to be based on determinants of sums of squares and products, which take the place of the reduced sums of squares appearing in the earlier examples.

Besides these detailed tests, it is also sometimes useful to make an over-all test of the adequacy of the given discriminant function. Such an over-all test has been described by Bartlett, Rao, and others. Although this test is not of such practical interest or so readily interpretable as the detailed tests, it is given below for completeness, and because it gives the simplest introduction to the methods of test.

To exemplify the general method we apply it to the further analysis of Barnard's data on Egyptian skulls.

Example 10.4 Further Examination of Data Presented in Example 10.2. In the treatment given in Example 10.2. no cognizance was taken of there being more than two series of skulls, only the regression of the characters on time being considered. We now consider the adequacy of the given function (i.e., time) to express the differences between series. Even if the regression of time on the skull measurements is significant, there are still the questions (i) whether any other variable representing a comparison among series has higher correlation with the skull measurements, and (ii) whether the different skull measurements conform with this discriminator, or whether more than one such comparison between series is needed to take into account the variation among the measurements. Tests of these questions will be called tests of direction and collinearity respectively.

It should be noted here that, whereas the hypothetical discriminator is usually a function of the independent variables (in particular, it may be one of them), in this example the "hypothetical discriminator" is a function of the group comparisons (i.e., time). However, on account of the duality mentioned in Section 10.2, this reversal of the roles of dependent and independent variables does not affect the analysis.

(i) The over-all test of time as a discriminator

The over-all test is a test of whether the simultaneous variation of x_1, x_2, x_3, and x_4 is linearly related to time, or whether there is significant departure from linearity. The test may be developed in the following way. Each of the sums of squares and products of the four variables may be partitioned into parts attributable to

	Degrees of Freedom
Regression on time	1
Deviation from regression	2
Residual	394
Residual plus deviation	396
Total	397

The relevant sums of squares and products are shown in Tables 10.14 and 10.15. Then, on the null hypothesis, the sums of squares and products for

TABLE 10.14

SUMS OF SQUARES AND PRODUCTS FOR DEVIATION FROM REGRESSION ON TIME
(Residual + deviation, 396 degrees of freedom)
(From Rao, Table 7d. 5ε)

x_1	x_2	x_3	x_4	T
⎡9665.25	449.01	1149.50	2142.20⎤	
449.01	9099.73	1265.69	2141.52	
1149.50	1265.69	4049.70	1203.30	
⎣2142.20	2141.52	1203.30	9257.37⎦	
				371.63

Determinant $= 2699.60 \times 10^{12}$

(deviation + residual), with 396 degrees of freedom, will be free of group differences after each variable has been adjusted for possible effects of each other one. This requirement may be expressed in the fact that the determinant of these sums of squares and products will be independent of group differences.

TABLE 10.15

SUMS OF SQUARES AND PRODUCTS FOR RESIDUAL

(394 degrees of freedom)

(From Rao, Table 7d. 5β)

x_1	x_2	x_3	x_4	T
9662.00	445.57	1130.62	2148.58	
445.57	9073.12	1239.22	2255.81	
1130.62	1239.22	3938.32	1271.05	
2148.58	2255.81	1271.05	8741.51	

335.80

Determinant = 2426.91 × 10¹²

This determinant can then be compared with the corresponding determinant for the residual sums of squares and products, and their ratio tested for significance.

If V = matrix of residual sums of squares and products

and Q = matrix of residual plus deviation sums of squares and products, the ratio is

$$R = \frac{|V|}{|Q|}.$$

This is called a (396:4, 2) determinantal ratio, to indicate the fact that there are 396 degrees of freedom in all, 4 independent variables, and 2 degrees of freedom between groups. In general, we would have a $(n - 1:p, q - 1)$ ratio. In view of the duality, ratios $(n:p, q)$ and $(n:q, p)$ have the same distribution.

In the present example, we see from Tables 10.14 and 10.15 that

$$|V| = 2426.91 \times 10^{12}$$

and

$$|Q| = 2699.60 \times 10^{12}$$

so that

$$R = 0.89899.$$

Small values of this ratio are significant. To test significance, we use a result of Rao (1951) that a $(n:p, q)$ is distributed like the sth power of a

$$\{s[n - \tfrac{1}{2}(p + q + 1)] + \tfrac{1}{2}pq + 1 : pq, 1\}$$

ratio, to a very close approximation. Here

$$s^2 = \frac{p^2q^2 - 4}{p^2 + q^2 - 5}.$$

The result is an identity when either p or q is one and is exact when p or q is two, as was proved by Wilks (1932).

In this case, since $q = 3$, we see that $R(n - 1:p, q - 1)$ is distributed as the square of a

$$(2n - 4:2p, 1) = (790:8, 1)$$

ratio. It may therefore be tested by the F test with 8 and 782 degrees of freedom:

$$F = \frac{782}{8} \frac{(1 - \sqrt{R})}{\sqrt{R}}$$

$$= \frac{782}{8} \frac{0.051\ 85}{0.948\ 15}$$

$$= 5.346 \text{ (significant at 1 per cent level).}$$

This is similar to the approximate result given by Rao (1952, page 271), for which

$$\chi^2 \ (8 \text{ D.F.}) = 40.02 \quad \text{(significant at 1 per cent level).}$$

Since the over-all test reveals departure from the linear relation with time, further analysis is of interest to see what this departure consists of.

(ii) The test for collinearity

The over-all criterion consists of two factors, one giving a test for departure from collinearity and the other giving a test for departure in direction. Two alternative factorizations are actually possible, analogous to the two different analyses for determining a simple and a partial regression coefficient. We consider first the factorization of the over-all criterion into a "simple direction" and a "partial collinearity" factor, which is appropriate for testing collinearity.

The regression function of t on the x variables, namely

$$T = b_1 x_1 + b_2 x_2 + b_3 x_3 + b_4 x_4,$$

is determined as the linear function of the x_i which minimizes the sum of squares for residual and deviation from regression as a whole. Accordingly, the sum of squares of T may be partitioned into parts for deviation and residual, with 2 and 394 degrees of freedom respectively, regardless of the fact that the regression coefficients are estimated from the data. This analysis of T provides the factor for "simple direction." The sums of squares for T required here are already shown in Tables 10.14 and 10.15. Thus we find for the "simple direction" ratio

$$(396:1, 2) = 335.80/371.63$$
$$= 0.90359.$$

Elimination of T reduces the total degrees of freedom and the number of x variables each by 1, so that for the "partial collinearity" factor we have

$$(395:3, 2) = 0.89899/0.90359$$
$$= 0.99491.$$

This ratio may now be tested by the F test (6 and 782 degrees of freedom):

$$F = \frac{782}{6} \frac{(1 - \sqrt{0.99491})}{\sqrt{0.99491}}$$

$$= \frac{782}{6} \frac{0.00255}{0.99745}$$

$$= 0.33.$$

Thus, there is no evidence for departure from collinearity in the data.

(iii) Test for direction

To test whether the direction of the hypothetical discriminator t is concordant with the data, we must analyze the regression function T, this time after eliminating the effect of the x variables which are orthogonal to it in the whole sample. The sums of squares for T, reduced thus, are determined both for the residual variation and for the residual plus deviation variation. The difference provides the criterion for testing departure of t in direction.

The actual calculation of the reduced sums of squares may be simplified by means of a device developed in Section 3.16. Suppose that the adjusted residual regression function of T on the x_i is

$$\sum_i a_i x_i.$$

Now the condition that T is uncorrelated with this function for the sample as a whole gives

$$\sum_h \sum_i a_i b_h t_{hi} = 0,$$

or

$$\sum_i a_i p_i = 0.$$

Then the reduced residual sum of squares is

$$\sum_h \sum_i (b_h - a_h)(b_i - a_i) v_{hi}$$

where the a_i are subject to this condition. Following the method given in Section 3.16, we find the minimized sum of squares to be

$$\frac{(\sum_i b_i p_i)^2}{\sum_h \sum_i p_h p_i v^{hi}}.$$

Here the v_{hi} are the sums of squares and products, within groups, of the x variables.

In exactly the same way, if the q_{hi} are the sums of squares and products for residual plus deviation variation, the corresponding reduced sum of squares of T is

$$\frac{(\sum_i b_i p_i)^2}{\sum_h \sum_i p_h p_i q^{hi}}.$$

Thus the partial direction criterion is

$$\frac{\sum_h \sum_i p_h p_i q^{hi}}{\sum_h \sum_i p_h p_i v^{hi}}.$$

A further simplification results from the fact that

$$\sum_h \sum_i p_h p_i q^{hi} = \frac{|T|}{|Q|} \sum_h \sum_i p_h p_i t^{hi}$$

$$= \frac{|T|}{|Q|} \sum_i b_i p_i$$

$$= \frac{S(t - \bar{t})^2 \sum_i b_i p_i}{S(t - \bar{t})^2 - \sum_i b_i p_i},$$

obviating the need for calculating the inverse elements q^{hi}.

Equivalent, though rather more elaborate, derivations have been given by Bartlett (1951) and Williams (1955); they are not, however, easily applicable to the present example.

In Table 10.16 the inverse of the matrix of residual sums of squares and

TABLE 10.16

INVERSE OF RESIDUAL MATRIX GIVEN IN TABLE 10.15

	x_1	x_2	x_3	x_4	$\sum_i p_i v^{hi}$
$10^{-6} \times$	111.806	4.158	−25.381	−24.863	0.082 337
	4.158	121.077	−30.299	−27.861	−0.159 390
	−25.381	−30.299	279.306	−26.555	0.158 416
	−24.863	−27.861	−26.555	131.559	−0.086 042
				$\sum_h \sum_i p_h p_i v^{hi}$	411.56

products is given, together with the derived sums of products used in forming $\sum_h \sum_i p_h p_i v^{hi}$. Hence the partial direction criterion is

$$\frac{4307.67 \times 371.63}{3936.04 \times 411.56} = 0.98824,$$

a (393:1, 2) ratio. To test this value we have

$$F = \frac{391}{2} \frac{(1 - 0.98824)}{0.98824}$$

$$= 2.33 \text{ (not significant)}.$$

This test of partial direction has been carried out to demonstrate the method of deriving such tests. In practice, if we may assume that the populations are collinear, we may then test the simple direction effect. This procedure is analogous to that for estimating and testing the constants in a multiple classification, on the assumption that interactions do not exist. The interaction sum of squares (analogous to the partial collinearity criterion) there provides the valid test for the existence of interactions. If interactions do not exist, the estimates of the constants and the sum of squares ignoring interactions (analogous to the simple direction criterion) would be used in any tests.

For the test of direction we therefore have, as before,

$$(396:1, 2) = 0.90359.$$

This may be transformed to an F ratio with 2 and 394 degrees of freedom:

$$F = \frac{394}{2} \frac{(1 - 0.90359)}{0.90359}$$

$$= 21.02 \text{ (significant at 1 per cent level)}.$$

Thus we conclude that, although a single discriminator is adequate to represent the variation in the four factors among the groups, time itself is not a satisfactory discriminator; in other words there is significant departure from linearity of regression on time.

10.8 COMMENTS ON THE ANALYSIS

It is interesting to compare the method of analysis outlined in Example 10.4 with that given by Bartlett (1947). In that analysis, a discriminant function in the x_i was determined to maximize the ratio of the regression sum of squares to the residual sum of squares, any other variation between groups (i.e., deviation from regression) being ignored. The analysis is therefore appropriate for testing the existence of a relationship, or of discrimination among series. The present analysis, on the other hand, gives a direct multiple regression of time on the x_i, which is appropriate for testing departure from regression, due to departure either in direction or from collinearity. In most cases the existence of the relationship may be taken for granted, so that it is relevant to test only the adequacy of the given function (in this case time) to represent the variation between series, by testing departure from regression.

10.9   GENERAL COMMENTS

As in multiple regression, so in discriminant analysis the work of calculation increases rapidly as the number of variables increases. Fortunately, however, we seldom find it necessary in practice to include more than four variables in either set.   If we make a satisfactory choice of variables, they will usually account for a major part of the association, any additional variables making a nonsignificant contribution.   Moreover, in discriminant analysis, the more variables included, the more likely it is that significant departures from collinearity will appear, so that the method will no longer be applicable (this is not, of course, a reason for excluding variables but a difficulty that will arise if they are included).

The examples included give some indication of the practical applications of discriminant analysis. As has been shown, even in complicated examples the mathematical theory and the calculations are not too difficult.   All the tests that are relevant for practical purposes are based on the null distribution either of variance ratios or, in the more complex cases, of determinantal ratios.   Thus, the far more difficult theory of the nonnull distributions, although possibly important from a mathematical point of view, is not relevant to these practical problems.

CHAPTER 11

Functional Relations

11.1 REGRESSION AND FUNCTIONAL RELATIONS

As has been explained in Chapter 1, there are important differences between regression relations, which express the expected value of one variable in terms of the observed values of other variables, and functional relations, which subsist between the expected values of different variables and will not therefore coincide with regression relations unless the independent variables are free from error. In general, functional relations are relations among the *parameters* of the distributions of different variables; but since we are here considering only linear relations among variables whose errors are normally distributed, we may describe the relations as relations among *expected values*.

When the independent variables are errorless, their observed and expected values coincide, so that the regression relation is the same as the functional relation, and both may be estimated by the method of least squares. In many of the examples discussed in previous chapters, the independent variables have been virtually free from error, so there has been no need to distinguish between the functional and the regression relation. (See, for example, the comparison of different theoretical relations, discussed in Chapter 6.) When the independent variables are subject to error, various special methods, to be described later, need to be used to estimate the functional relation. A detailed discussion of the estimation of linear functional relations has been given by Lindley (1947).

Not only do linear functional relations differ from regression relations in general, but they also have different applications. The regression relation is the more generally useful, relating as it does to observed values; its main application is to the prediction of either observed or expected values of one variable from observed values of the others. In most practical applications the regression and not the functional relation is required.

Before considering methods of estimation, therefore, we need to consider in what circumstances the functional relation is relevant. Thus a theory may specify some relation among the underlying or expected values of certain variables. It would then be of interest to determine whether the data support the specified form of relationship, as well as to estimate the parameters of the relationship or to check the concordance of given parametric values with the observations. It is only rarely that the form of such a relationship can be deduced from observed values, although the form, once decided from theoretical considerations, can often be verified or contradicted by the observations.

The regression relations are based on the variation in both the "true" values and the random errors to which the observations are subject, the functional relation on the variation in the "true" values alone. A little reflection will show (and examination of the literature will confirm; see, for example, Haavelmo (1943)) that the functional relation is therefore relevant only to a study of how the "true" values of both variables are affected by some extraneous variable or variables; that is to say, the relationship shows what elements of the system are invariant under changes in conditions. It is not of interest to know the underlying relation (if any) between two variables when each is affected only by random error; usually what is then wanted is one or the other of the regression relations.

In calibration experiments, where one measuring instrument is being checked against another, the linear functional relation between the results given by the two instruments is required. For we are here concerned with the underlying relation between the results, persisting through changes in conditions (in this case, the properties of the materials being measured), and regardless of the random errors to which the results may be subject. Generally it will be required that one instrument be capable of replacing the other under a wide range of conditions. For example, in paper testing, the tear tester measures an arbitrarily defined property of the paper. The calibration of a new instrument against the standard requires that the new instrument give readings for various weights of paper that are roughly linearly related to those given by the standard. Clearly, the greater the range of qualities and weights of paper, the less the relative contribution of experimental error to the total variation of the results, and the more closely the two regression equations will approach the functional relation; but since, in general, each regression will differ from the functional relation, it is preferable to determine the latter directly.

Since the values of regression coefficients are affected by the magnitudes of the errors in the independent variables, these coefficients are useless for examining the concordance of a set of data with a theoretical relationship; for this purpose the functional relation needs to be estimated. Moreover, in different sets of data in which the same underlying relationship is believed to hold, the regression coefficients may be affected to varying extents by the presence of random variation in the independent variables; the magnitude of this effect depends on the ratio of the variance introduced by random error to the variance of the "true" values. In such cases there will be differences among the regression coefficients that are not a reflection of any variation in the underlying relationship. In this case, too, the functional relation needs to be estimated for each set of data in order to test its constancy over all sets.

Hitherto we have been discussing the estimation of the constants in a linear functional relation, in which the variables included, although subject to error, are given. In other uses of the functional relations, the problem of estimation arises in another way. Suppose, for example, that a linear function, such as an "index number," has been defined for a certain set of variables. The constants are given, but it is desired to adjust these constants, if possible, to allow for the fact that the different variables in the linear function have differing accuracy. This problem was solved by Yates (1939a), who showed that, although the index number with unadjusted constants is of course unbiased, greater accuracy is achieved if the multipliers of the less accurately determined variables are reduced numerically from their theoretical values. The method also has applications in plant and animal breeding, where selection indexes are estimated in a similar way.

11.2   ESTIMATION OF A LINEAR FUNCTIONAL RELATION

It is well known that, when both the "true" values and the errors are normally distributed, the functional relation cannot be determined from data. Lindley (1947), Reiersøl (1950), and others have obtained a number of results which show that the nonnormality of one of the distributions is necessary for the estimation of the relationship to be possible. Thus it may be taken that functional relations are not determinable from the internal analysis of a set of variables with normal distributions. Put in another way, since the first- and second-order sample moments summarize all the information in samples from normal populations, it follows that information beyond that on the first- and second-order moments of the distributions must be available if the functional relation is to be determinable. This information may be present in the sample, if the distribution is not normal, for then the first- and second-order sample moments are no longer sufficient statistics for the parameters of the distribution; alternatively, it may be introduced through knowledge of the relation of each variable with some extraneous variables. As mentioned before, it is only in such circumstances, when some such additional information exists, that the functional relation is of interest; in other words, whenever functional relations are of practical interest, they are also determinable from data.

In passing, it may be mentioned that Berkson's (1950) method of "controlled variables," as elucidated by Lindley (1953), is a specification of the experimental technique which enables one variable to be dealt with as though it were errorless. Thus the estimation of the functional relation is in such cases reduced to the estimation of a regression equation. The method will be discussed further.

(i) Methods Based on Properties of the Distribution

In most branches of applied statistics it is convenient to assume that the underlying error distribution is normal because it simplifies the calculations without greatly affecting the validity of the conclusions drawn from the analysis. However, in the determination of functional relations, the assumption of normality is a positive handicap. On this assumption it is not possible to estimate the relationship at all.

If we can assume some form of departure of the distribution of the variables from normality, we can validly estimate the relationship (Neyman and Scott, 1951). Many such methods use moments of the distributions higher than the second. However, any result whose validity has to be based on the assumption of a certain form for the distribution, or even on the existence of certain higher moments of the distribution, is not fully satisfactory. It seems preferable to base the estimation on methods that make minimal assumptions about the form of the distribution—except where for computational convenience we assume normality. We need, in fact, to provide ourselves with information additional to that obtained from observations on the variables we are investigating. This additional information may be provided in various ways, some of which we now give.

(ii) Ratio of Error Variances Known

In many experiments, for example those on the calibration of a new instrument against a standard, it is to be expected that the error variances of the readings given by the two instruments are equal; more generally, in other cases the error variances may be in some ratio which is determinable from physical considerations. In such experiments there is effectively but one error to be determined, and valid estimation is possible.

Consider a sample of n pairs of values of variables x_1, x_2, and assume, without loss of generality, that their error variances are equal. If it is assumed that their expected values are linearly related, this may be expressed by saying that a linear function of x_1 and x_2 is distributed with constant mean and unit variance. Such a linear function will be called a null variate, because the systematic component of its variation vanishes. Suppose that the null variate is

$$\xi = x_1 + \gamma x_2.$$

Then the variance of ξ is proportional to

$$1 + \gamma^2.$$

We must now minimize, with respect to γ, the sum of squares

$$\frac{S[x_1 - \bar{x} + \gamma(x_2 - \bar{x}_2)]^2}{1 + \gamma^2} = \frac{t_{11} + 2\gamma t_{12} + \gamma^2 t_{22}}{1 + \gamma^2},$$

which leads to the equation

$$\gamma^2 t_{12} + \gamma(t_{11} - t_{22}) - t_{12} = 0. \tag{11.1}$$

The two roots of this equation, which we denote by c_1 and c_2, represent orthogonal directions, so that the sums of squares of the corresponding linear forms constitute a partition of the sums of squares of x_1 and x_2 about their means, namely $t_{11} + t_{22}$. Since $c_2 = -1/c_1$, we have

$$\frac{c_1^2 t_{11} - 2c_1 t_{12} + t_{22}}{1 + c_1^2} + \frac{t_{11} + 2c_1 t_{12} + c_1^2 t_{22}}{1 + c_1^2} = t_{11} + t_{22}. \tag{11.2}$$

The two terms on the left-hand side of (11.2) are the maximum and the minimum sum of squares for any linear form, which may be identified with the sum of squares among the true values and the sum of squares of residuals, respectively. The relevant estimate c_1 is the one that minimizes the residual sum of squares.

Although equation (11.1) gives the appropriate estimate of the constant in the relationship, it does not enable fiducial limits for the constant to be determined. These limits may be determined in the following way. Since x_1 and x_2 are subject to independent errors of equal variance, it follows that the null variate

$$\xi = x_1 + \gamma x_2$$

is uncorrelated with the variate

$$\xi' = \gamma x_1 - x_2,$$

provided the null hypothesis is true. Hence the sample regression of ξ on ξ' should differ from zero only by sampling error. Accordingly, if the regression of ξ on ξ' is significant, it indicates that the hypothetical value of γ is not concordant with the data. It may be verified that the estimates c_1 and c_2 are those values of γ for which the regression of ξ on ξ' vanishes. We then have the analysis of variance of ξ shown in Table 11.1.

It will be noted that this analysis has the same form as the analysis for testing the abscissa of concurrent regression lines (Chapter 8). It is, in fact, another example of a general type of analysis for problems of this

TABLE 11.1

	D.F.	Sum of Squares
Constant (regression on ξ')	1	$\dfrac{(\gamma^2 t_{12} + \gamma(t_{11} - t_{22}) - t_{12})^2}{\gamma^2 t_{11} - 2\gamma t_{12} + t_{22}}$
Residual	$n - 2$	$\dfrac{(1 + \gamma^2)^2(t_{11}t_{22} - t_{12}{}^2)}{\gamma^2 t_{11} - 2\gamma t_{12} + t_{22}}$
Total	$n - 1$	$t_{11} + 2\gamma t_{12} + \gamma^2 t_{22}$

kind, in which the null hypothesis specifies not only a null variate but in effect an "explanatory variate," in the sense of covariance analysis, as well.

Example 11.1 The Comparison of Two Measures of a Strength Property of Timber. The Izod test is a test of the impact strength of materials. The test was applied to specimens of wood cut from 109 planks of Northern Silver Ash; each plank provided two specimens, of which one was tested radially, the other tangentially to the growth rings. The question at issue was whether the systematic components of radial Izod and tangential Izod differed significantly in magnitude. In making this test it was assumed that the variance due to random variations was the same for each variable; this is reasonable, since both result from the same method of test. The sums of squares and products of the test results were as follows:

$$t_{11} = 1232$$
$$t_{12} = 1086$$
$$t_{22} = 1543,$$

each with 108 degrees of freedom, the suffixes 1 and 2 referring to radial and tangential Izod respectively. For estimating the constant in the relationship we have the equation

$$1086\gamma^2 - 311\gamma - 1086 = 0,$$

giving
$$c_1 = -0.8670$$
$$c_2 = +1.1534.$$

The value c_1 is clearly the required coefficient of proportionality, showing that the systematic component of x_1 is somewhat less than that of x_2. To test the significance of departure of this value from the hypothetical value -1, we substitute in the formal analysis of variance just given. Then the total sum of squares is

$$1232 - 2(1086) + 1543 = 603,$$

and the sum of squares for departure of the constant from its hypothetical value is

$$\frac{(1232 - 1543)^2}{1232 + 2(1086) + 1543} = \frac{311^2}{4947} = 19.55.$$

The analysis of variance is shown in Table 11.2.

TABLE 11.2

	D.F.	Sum of Squares	Mean Square
Constant	1	19.55	19.55
Residual	107	583.45	5.453
Total	108	603	

The F ratio, with 1 and 107 degrees of freedom, is 3.59, not significant, so that we are not justified in assuming that the systematic components of the two variables differ in magnitude. Whether the variables can be regarded as equivalent in other respects is, however, beyond the scope of the present test and cannot be answered from these data.

It will be seen later that the situation in which the ratio of variances is known is a particular case of a much more commonly occurring one, in which the variances of the random components are estimated from residual sums of squares. If the systematic variance in the variables is associated with some groupings of the data, or with some extraneous variables, the sums of squares within groups, or about the regression on these extraneous variables, will provide estimates of the random component of the variances. The analysis in these situations is similar, allowance having to be made for the errors in estimation of these residual variances.

It will also be noted that the problem of finding fiducial limits of a ratio, which was discussed in Chapter 6, is really a special case of the determination of a functional relation, in which there is no constant term.

(iii) Error Variances Known

When the error variance of one of the variables (say, x_2) is known, we can determine a consistent estimate of the coefficient in the functional relation. On the assumption that the errors in x_1 and x_2 are independent, it is clear that the sum of products of x_1 and x_2 is an unbiased estimate of the sum of products of the "true values." On the other hand, the sum of squares of x_2 will be inflated by an amount proportional to the error variance and the degrees of freedom. Hence, if the error variance is known, the sum of squares may be adjusted to give an unbiased estimate of the sum of squares of the "true values." Thus, if the variance is σ^2, the adjusted sum of squares for a sample of size n will be

$$t_{22} - (n - 1)\sigma^2$$

and the estimate of the constant γ will be

$$c = -t_{12}/[t_{22} - (n - 1)\sigma^2].$$

This method is satisfactory only when n is large, for the adjusted sum of squares may sometimes be negative as a result of sampling fluctuations, and the probability of this occurrence will be negligible only when n is large.

This method of adjusting for the errors in variables may be adapted for use when estimates of the error variances are given. When the variation can be analyzed into the variance within and between groups, the mean square between groups may be adjusted by deducting the mean square within groups; the difference generally provides an unbiased estimate of the variance of the "true values," provided, of course, that these are associated with group differences. This method has found some applications in genetics (see, for example, Smith, 1936).

Another potential application in economics and other fields has been discussed by Yates (1939a). In setting up an index number to measure a trend or other characteristic of a series, we often use a linear combination of several variables with given weights. If these variables are inaccurately measured, the question arises whether some allowance can be made by adjustment of the weights for the differing accuracies of different variables. Yates shows that if the error variances and the variances of the true values are known, a suitable adjustment is possible. Roughly speaking, its effect is to reduce the weights attached to the less accurate variables. Needless to say, in making such an analysis, the underlying assumptions must be borne in mind. Thus, with time series data, it may not be appropriate to consider the true values as having come from a single population, since conditions may change systematically over the period. Nevertheless, some over-all improvement is possible in such an index by adjusting the coefficients suitably.

The method of adjustment is to choose the linear function of the *observed* values so that the variance of the difference between that linear function and the index based on the true values is a minimum. This analysis is, of course, possible only if some estimates are available of the variances and covariances of the true values. These can often be obtained from an analysis of data that permit classification into several groups corresponding to different true values.

(iv) Controlled Variables

A situation that must frequently arise in practice is one in which the independent variables, although subject to error, are controlled. Here, although the variables are subject to error, the linear functional relation can be estimated without bias from the regression equation.

When the independent variable is an observation such as a meter reading which is subject to random errors of measurement, the experimenter, in trying to take observations corresponding to assigned values of the independent variable, will be able to control the observed values but not the true values. For example, in applying a load to a test specimen as in determining the relation of load and time to failure, the load may be set at some predetermined level. The observed load is then fixed, but the actual load may vary about that observed as a result of experimental errors, inaccuracies in the setting and in the dimensions of the specimen, and so on. In such cases, however, although the measurements are subject to error, the errors are uncorrelated with the observed values, being in fact correlated with the true values. The model of variation is thus different from that usually specified in applications of the method of least squares. It can then be shown that the regression coefficients are unbiased estimates of the constants in the linear functional relation. The variances of the regression coefficients are found in the usual way. Since the variances of the observed values will be less than the variances among the true values, the variances of the regression coefficients will in general be greater than they would have been had the variables been errorless.

Regression equations based on controlled variables can be used for prediction. Needless to say, in later applications of the regression equation the independent variables would need to be controlled variables. In application to inverse estimation the estimates and fiducial limits obtained would apply to the values of the controlled variables (e.g., meter readings), which are what would normally be required; fiducial limits for the true values, if required for any reason, would be somewhat wider.

The distinction between controlled variables and variables otherwise subject to error has been noted comparatively recently. This may be due to the fact that variables are most frequently thus controlled in the physical sciences, where it has been found satisfactory to treat the independent variables as errorless.

(v) The Method of Grouping

Another method for determining the functional relation between two variables, described by Wald (1940) and Bartlett (1949), uses groupings of the variables. The basis of the method is that, if the values can be separated into a few large distinct groups, the means of the variables within each group will be little affected by random variation, and the differences among the group means will be due to systematic variation. Wald divides the data into two groups of equal size according to the magnitude of values of one of the independent variables, and takes the line joining the points of means of the two groups as the estimate of the functional relation. Bartlett derives an estimate of the constant of proportionality with somewhat smaller variance by dividing the data into three equal or nearly equal groups in the same way and determining the slope of the line joining the points of means of the extreme groups.

These methods are open to the objection, not always serious in practice, that the group limits are based on the observed values and not on some external criterion defining systematic differences. Neyman and Scott (1951) have shown that only "in very exceptional circumstances" does the method provide consistent estimates. Roughly speaking, the method leads to consistent estimates if the separation of values of one of the variates is sufficiently wide in the neighborhood of the group limits that a grouping based on observed values is equivalent to a grouping based on true values. Clearly, under these conditions, the differences between groups may be attributed to some extraneous variates. Hence, the method of grouping, when valid, is best considered as one of the methods in which the systematic variation of each of the variables under consideration is associated with extraneous variables. These methods we shall now consider.

11.3 ESTIMATION BY MEANS OF INSTRUMENTAL VARIABLES

It was pointed out in Section 11.2 that functional relationships among a set of variables are most often of interest when they reflect the elements of the set that are invariant under changes in extraneous variables. Consequently, in many practical studies of functional relations, the relation of the variables under study with some extraneous variables are examined. An appropriate method of estimating functional relations is to determine the linear functions of the set that are uncorrelated with the extraneous variables. These linear functions will then define the relationships. The extraneous variables will be called *instrumental* variables (Reiersøl, 1941, 1945) to distinguish them from the *investigational* variables.

We shall henceforth consider only the estimation of a single relationship. Bartlett (1948) has given an interesting example of the determination and use of two simultaneous relations among a set of variables. It can be seen that, if there are p investigational variables, we require at least $p - 1$ instrumental variables in order to estimate the relationship. We shall suppose that there are, in general, p investigational variables x_i and q instrumental variables y_j. The instrumental variables may be differences among $q + 1$ groups, so that the formal regression on the q variables will be equivalent in such cases to an analysis of variance within and between groups.

Suppose that the functional relationship is defined by the null variate

$$\xi = \sum_i \gamma_i x_i$$

being uncorrelated with the y_j. We may standardize the scale of the coefficients by specifying that

$$\sum_h \sum_i \gamma_h \gamma_i t_{hi} = 1,$$

so that there are but $p - 1$ independent coefficients. The sum of squares for regression of ξ on the q y_j then provides a test for the concordance of the coefficients with the data. We write

$p_{\xi j}$ sum of products of ξ and y_j;

then the sum of squares for regression is

$$\sum_j \sum_k p_{\xi j} p_{\xi k} u^{jk}$$

and the total sum of squares for ξ is

$$\sum_h \sum_i \gamma_h \gamma_i t_{hi} = 1.$$

Then the analysis of variance for testing the assigned coefficients takes the following form given in Table 11.3.

TABLE 11.3

	D.F.	Sum of Squares
Regression (test of assigned coefficients)	q	$\sum_j \sum_k p_{\xi j} p_{\xi k} u^{jk}$
Residual	$n - q - 1$	$1 - \sum_j \sum_k p_{\xi j} p_{\xi k} u^{jk}$
Total	$n - 1$	1

This analysis is satisfactory for testing the concordance of any assigned values of the coefficients with the data. For the estimation of the coefficients, however, the analysis differs slightly according as q is less than, equal to, or greater than $p - 1$.

(i) $q = p - 1$

Since there are $p - 1$ independent coefficients and the regression sum of squares has $p - 1$ degrees of freedom, we may estimate the coefficients by equating the regression sum of squares to zero. Alternatively, and more directly, we get $p - 1$ simultaneous equations by equating the sum of products of ξ with each of the y_j (i.e., the $p_{\xi j}$) to zero. The equations are

$$\sum_i \gamma_i p_{ij} = 0 \qquad (j = 1, 2, \cdots, p - 1)$$

The solutions of these equations will be denoted by c_i.

(ii) $q < p - 1$

When the number of instrumental variables is less than $p - 1$, we can still determine the regression of the null variate ξ on these variates and then set up an analysis to test the concordance of the coefficients with the data. It will not be possible, however, to determine a unique null function from the sample, since it will be possible to determine $p - q$ independent linear functions of the x_i which are uncorrelated with the y_j. Thus, although we can test a given null variate, we cannot estimate one uniquely from the sample.

(iii) $q > p - 1$

In this case, because the sum of squares for regression has more than $p - 1$ degrees of freedom, it will not, in general, vanish for any choice of the coefficients in the null variate. To estimate the coefficients from the data, we choose them to minimize the regression sum of squares. The equations of estimation are nonlinear, so that the sum of squares thus minimized, although it has $q - p + 1$ degrees of freedom, is not distributed as a sum of squares of independent normal variables. This sum of squares nevertheless provides an approximate test of the residual correlation of the x_i with the y_j. If this is significant, we must conclude that there is no null variate; that is, there is no underlying functional relation that persists for varying values of the y_j.

It can be shown that the sum of squares for regression, minimized with respect to the coefficients γ_i, is the smallest root θ of the determinantal equation

$$\left| \sum_j \sum_k p_{hj} p_{ik} u^{jk} - \theta t_{hi} \right| = 0,$$

which may be written

$$|PU^{-1}P' - \theta T| = 0.$$

The coefficients c_i are the elements of the corresponding characteristic vector.

Since the $p_{\xi j}$ have zero expectations, they may be regarded as values of a new null variate, and the sum of squares for regression can then be regarded as the sum of squares of this null variate. Various aspects of the variation among the $p_{\xi j}$ may be studied. It would be advantageous if the sum of squares could be separated into two parts: a sum of squares, with $p - 1$ degrees of freedom, representing departures of the assigned coefficients from those given by the data (test of direction); and (when $q > p - 1$) one with $q - p + 1$ degrees of freedom, representing the minimal association between the x variables and y variables. Such an exact analysis does not seem to be possible, however; for if it were, it would correspond to a partition due to the regression of the null variate $p_{\xi j}$ on $p - 1$ "explanatory" variates. From a knowledge of the null variate it is not possible, however, to define such a set of explanatory variates. Consequently, only approximate tests are possible.

When the error variances and covariances are based on a large number of degrees of freedom, these variances and covariances may be taken as known exactly, and then the analysis follows the lines given in Section 11.3, (ii).

Example 11.2 Calibration of Bending Mandrel against Cold Check Tests of Lacquer Surfaces. Schrumpf, Carter, and Hader (1956) report the results of an experiment in which the check resistance of lacquer surfaces was tested by two methods, one giving the average number of cycles of flexing before surface failure, the other giving the diameter of the mandrel over which the specimen was bent for failure. Seven different lacquers, of differing composition (percentage hard lacquer), were tested; the percentage of hard lacquer is thus the instrumental variable for this experiment. Although the number of results is small, and the fiducial limits for the constant in the relationship correspondingly wide, this experiment illustrates well the use of an instrumental variable to calibrate the tests.

The experimental data are set out in Table 11.4. Table 11.5 gives the matrix of sums of squares and products of average cycles (x_1), mandrel size (x_2), and composition (y), and Table 11.6 gives the analysis of variance and covariance of x_1 and x_2.

The null variate being $x_1 + \gamma x_2$, we find for the sample estimate of the constant

$$c = -p_1/p_2$$
$$= 146.51/11.925$$
$$= 12.29.$$

The calibration equation is

$$X_1 = 15.44 - 12.29 X_2.$$

TABLE 11.4

CHECK RESISTANCE OF LACQUER SURFACES: CALIBRATION OF BENDING
MANDREL AGAINST COLD CHECK TESTS

Average Number of Cycles, x_1	Average Mandrel Diameter, x_2, in.	Composition, y, percentage hard
2.2	1.017	32.0
5.6	0.892	25.5
7.2	0.617	20.0
9.9	0.558	16.5
9.6	0.417	14.0
10.4	0.442	12.5
11.3	0.283	11.0
Total 56.2	4.226	131.5

TABLE 11.5

SUMS OF SQUARES AND PRODUCTS OF VALUES IN TABLE 11.4

$$\begin{array}{ccc} x_1 & x_2 & y \\ \left[\begin{array}{cc} 62.85 & -4.932 \\ -4.932 & 0.4201 \end{array}\right] & & \begin{array}{c} -146.51 \\ 11.925 \end{array} \\ & & 349.43 \end{array}$$

TABLE 11.6

ANALYSIS OF VARIANCE AND COVARIANCE FOR x_1 AND x_2

		Sums of Squares and Products		
	D.F.	x_1^2	$x_1 x_2$	x_2^2
Regression on y	1	61.43	−5.000	0.4070
Residual	5	1.42	+0.068	0.0131
Total	6	62.85	−4.932	0.4201

The 1 per cent point for F with 1 and 5 degrees of freedom is 16.26. The fiducial limits for γ are therefore the roots of the equation

$$\frac{5(61.43 - 10.000\gamma + 0.4070\gamma^2)}{1.42 + 0.136\gamma + 0.0131\gamma^2} = 16.26,$$

that is,

$$7.3 \text{ and } 21.4.$$

References

Alexander, G., and R. H. Watson (1951). The assay of oestrogenic activity of *Trifolium subterraneum* L. by increase in uterine weight in the spayed guinea pig. I. Characteristics of the dose-response-relationship. *Aust. J. Agric. Res.*, 2, 457–479.

Anderson, T. W. (1958). *An Introduction to Multivariate Statistical Analysis.* Wiley, New York.

Barnard, M. M. (1935). The secular variations of skull characters in four series of Egyptian skulls. *Ann. Eugen., Lond.*, 6, 352–371.

Bartlett, M. S. (1947). Multivariate analysis. *J. Roy. Stat. Soc., Suppl.*, 9, 176–190.

—— (1948). A note on the statistical estimation of supply and demand relations from time series. *Econometrica*, 16, 323–329.

—— (1949). Fitting a straight line when both variables are subject to error. *Biometrics*, 5, 207–212.

—— (1951). Goodness of fit of a single hypothetical discriminant function in the case of several groups. *Ann. Eugen., Lond.*, 16, 199–214.

Berkson, J. (1950). Are there two regressions? *J. Amer. Stat. Assoc.*, 45, 164–180.

Box, G. E. P. and J. S. Hunter (1954). A confidence region for the solution of a set of simultaneous equations with an application to experimental design. *Biometrika*, 41, 190–199.

Carter, A. H. (1949). The estimation and comparison of residual regressions where there are two or more related sets of observations. *Biometrika*, 36, 26–46.

Cochran, W. G. (1938). The omission or addition of an independent variate in multiple linear regression. *J. Roy. Stat. Soc., Suppl.*, 2, 171–176.

Cohen, W. E. and A. W. Mackney (1951). Influence of wood extractives on soda and sulphate pulping. *Proc. Aust. Pulp Paper Ind. Tech. Assoc.*, 5, 315–335.

Crout, P. D. (1941). A short method for evaluating determinants and solving systems of linear equations with real or complex coefficients. *Trans. A.I.E.E.*, 60, 1235–1241.

Day, B. B. (1937). A suggested method for allocating logging costs to log sizes. *J. For.*, 35, 69–71.

—— and M. M. Sandomire (1942). Use of the discriminant function for more than two groups. *J. Amer. Stat. Assoc.*, 37, 461–472.

Ditchburne, N. (1959). The interpretation of data on time to failure of specimens under load. Submitted for publication.

Durbin, J. (1953). A note on regression when there is extraneous information about one of the coefficients. *J. Amer. Stat. Assoc.*, 48, 799–808.

Finney, D. J. (1946). Standard errors of yields adjusted for regression on an independent measurement. *Biometrics*, 2, 53–55.

—— (1952). *Statistical Methods in Biological Assay.* Griffin, London.

Fisher, Hans, R. G. Hansen, and H. W. Norton (1955). Quantitative determination of glucose and galactose. *Anal. Chem.*, 27, 857–859.

209

Fisher, R. A. (1951). *The Design of Experiments.* 6th Edition. Oliver and Boyd, Edinburgh.

—— (1954). *Statistical Methods for Research Workers.* 12th Edition. Oliver and Boyd, Edinburgh.

—— (1956). *Statistical Methods and Scientific Inference.* Hafner, New York.

—— and F. Yates (1953). *Statistical Tables for Biological, Agricultural and Medical Research.* 4th Edition. Oliver and Boyd, Edinburgh.

Haavelmo, T. (1943). The statistical implications of a system of simultaneous equations. *Econometrica*, 11, 1–12.

Hartley, H. O. (1948). The estimation of non-linear parameters by "internal least squares." *Biometrika*, 35, 32–45.

Hasel, A. A. (1946). Logging cost as related to tree size and intensity of cutting in ponderosa pine. *J. For.*, 44, 552–560.

Hoel, P. G. (1947). On the choice of forecasting formulas. *J. Amer. Stat. Assoc.*, 42, 605–611.

Hotelling, H. (1939). Tubes and spheres in n-spaces and a class of statistical problems. *Amer. J. Math.*, 61, 440–460.

—— (1940). The selection of variates for use in prediction with some comments on the general problem of nuisance parameters. *Ann. Math. Stat.*, 11, 271–283.

—— (1941). Experimental determination of the maximum of a function. *Ann. Math. Stat.*, 12, 20–45.

Keeping, E. S. (1951). A significance test for exponential regression. *Ann. Math. Stat.*, 22, 180–198.

Kullback, S. and H. M. Rosenblatt (1957). On the analysis of multiple regression in k categories. *Biometrika*, 44, 67–83.

Lawrence, A. J. (1955). The determination of total solids in skim milk concentrates by the refractometer. *Aust. J. Dairy Tech.*, 10, 6–7.

Lindley, D. V. (1947). Regression lines and the linear functional relationship. *J. Roy. Stat. Soc., Suppl.*, 9, 218–244.

—— (1953). Estimation of a functional relationship. *Biometrika*, 40, 47–49.

Littler, G. F. and B. Adkins (1954). The milling of hardwoods in South East Queensland. *Queensland Forest Service Research Notes*, No. 1.

Neyman, J. (1954). Comments in the "Discussion on the Symposium on Interval Estimation." *J. Roy. Stat. Soc.*, B16, 216–218.

—— and E. L. Scott (1951). On certain methods of estimating the linear structural relation. *Ann. Math. Stat.*, 22, 352–361.

Pimentel-Gomes, F. (1953). The use of Mitscherlich's regression law in the analysis of experiments with fertilizers. *Biometrics*, 9, 498–516.

Rao, C. R. (1951). An asymptotic expansion of the distribution of Wilks' Λ criterion. *Bull. Internat. Stat. Inst.*, 33, Part II, 177–180.

—— (1952). *Advanced Statistical Methods in Biometric Research.* Wiley, New York.

Reiersøl, O. (1941). Confluence analysis by means of lag moments and other methods of confluence analysis. *Econometrica*, 9, 1–22.

—— (1945). Confluence analysis by means of instrumental sets of variables. *Ark. Mat. Astr. Fys.*, 32A, No. 4, 1–119.

—— (1950). Identifiability of a linear relation between variables which are subject to error. *Econometrica*, 18, 375–389.

Roy, S. N. (1957). *Some Aspects of Multivariate Analysis.* Wiley, New York.

Scheffé, H. (1953). A method for judging all contrasts in the analysis of variance. *Biometrika*, 40, 87–104.

Schrumpf, W. M., R. M. Carter and R. J. Hader (1956). A rapid method of evaluating check resistance of furniture lacquer films. *Fed. Paint and Varnish Prod. Clubs Official Digest*, 28, 79–89.

Schumacher, F. X. and W. C. Jones (1940). Empirical log rules and the allocation of sawing time to log size. *J. For.* 38, 889–896.

Smith, H. Fairfield (1936). A discriminant function for plant selection. *Ann. Eugen., Lond.*, 7, 240–250.

Snedecor, G. W. (1956). *Statistical Methods Applied to Experiments in Agriculture and Biology*. 5th Edition. Iowa State College Press, Ames, Iowa.

Stevens, W. L. (1951). Asymptotic regression. *Biometrics*, 7, 247–267.

Sulzberger, P. H. (1953). The effect of temperature on the strength of wood, plywood and glued joints. Aeronautical Research Consultative Committee, Australia. Dept. of Supply, Report ACA-46.

Tocher, K. D. (1952). On the concurrence of a set of regression lines. *Biometrika*, 39, 109–117.

van der Waerden, B. L. (1931). *Moderne Algebra*. Springer, Berlin.

Wald, A. (1940). The fitting of straight lines if both variables are subject to error. *Ann. Math. Stat.*, 11, 284–300.

Wilks, S. S. (1932). Certain generalizations in the analysis of variance. *Biometrika*, 24, 471–494.

—— (1946). Sample criteria for testing equality of means, equality of variances, and equality of covariances in a normal multivariate distribution. *Ann. Math. Stat.*, 17, 257–281.

Williams, E. J. (1953). Tests of significance for concurrent regression lines. *Biometrika*, 40, 297–305.

—— (1954). Estimation of components of variability. C.S.I.R.O., Australia. Division of Mathematical Statistics. Technical Paper No. 1.

—— (1955). Significance tests for discriminant functions and linear functional relationships. *Biometrika*, 42, 360–381.

—— and N. H. Kloot (1953). Interpolation in a series of correlated observations. *Aust. J. Appl. Sci.*, 4, 1–17.

Yates, F. (1939a). The adjustment of the weights of compound index numbers based on inaccurate data. *J. Roy. Stat. Soc.*, 102, 285–288.

—— (1939b). Tests of significance of the differences between regression coefficients derived from two sets of correlated variates. *Proc. Roy. Soc. Edin.*, 59, 184–194.

—— (1951). The influence of *Statistical Methods for Research Workers* on the development of the science of statistics. *J. Amer. Stat. Assoc.*, 46, 19–34.

Index

Addition of independent variable, 34
Adjusted, sum of squares, 123, 132
  treatment effects, 122
Adjustment, empirical, 117
  for addition or omission of independ-
    ent variable, 35
  to trial value, 61
Adkins, B., 107
Alexander, G., 133
Allocation, 22
Anderson, T. W., 3

Barnard, M. M., 175, 176, 182
Bartlett, M. S., 183, 187, 192, 193, 203,
  204
Berkson, J., 198
Box, G. E. P., 162

Calibration, 3, 10, 65, 90, 105, 163,
  196, 198
Carter, A. H., 151, 152
Carter, R. M., 207
Check column, 29
Cochran, W. G., 34, 35
Coefficients, test of assigned, 13, 37, 61,
  81, 179, 184, 205
  variances and covariances of, 25
  in simultaneous equations, 164
  restricted, 52, 86
Cohen, W. E., 102
Coincidence, test of, 132
Collinearity, of populations, 185
  test for, 190
Comparison, of correlations, 73
  of regression equations, 129, 151
  of theoretical formulas, 81, 83

Comparisons, multiple, 5, 8
Complex roots, interpretation of, 92,
  108, 114
Concurrent regressions, 49, 137
  abscissa of, 142
  departure from, 139
  ordinate of, 139
Conditional test, 79
Consistency of simultaneous equations,
  166, 170
Controlled variables, 198, 203
Controls, 52
Corrections, 37
Correlated data, 149, 151
Correlation, coefficient of, 25, 73
Correlations, comparison of, 73
Covariance, adjustment, 119
  analysis of, 3, 94, 132
  in significance testing, 128, 141,
    149, 185, 200
Criterion, most predictable, 165
Crout, P. D., 25, 27, 28, 33, 34
Curve fitting, 41

Daily total method, 107
Day, B. B., 107, 176
Departure from, collinearity, 190
  concurrence, 139
  hypothetical discriminator, 179, 191
  linear compound, 85
  linear restriction, 51
  origin, 14, 45
  proportionality, 150
Dependent variable, 11
Determinantal ratio, 189
Determination, coefficient of, 25

Deviation from regression, linear, 16, 121, 188
  adjusted, 123
  nonlinear, 64
Difference of regressions, 123, 127
Direct probability, 91
Direct product, 167
Direction, of population differences, 185
  test for, 191, 207
Discriminant analysis, 3, 128
  function, 93, 171, 175, 183
Ditchburne, N., 159
Duality, 188
Durbin, J., 158

Effective reduced variance, 125
Environmental variable, 118
Estimation, direct, 95, 164
  from nonlinear equations, 105
  inverse, 91, 95, 166
  of coefficients, 12, 24
  of discriminant functions, 177
  of functional relations, 197, 204
  of nonlinear equations, 60
  restricted, 50
Exclusive fiducial limits, 93
Explanatory variable, 118, 125, 128, 142, 149, 200, 207
Exponential regression, 61, 62

Fiducial, boundary, 36
  "distribution," 92
  limits, 8, 36, 93, 95
    inverse, 96, 169
    simultaneous, 36, 169, 184
  probability, 91
  range, 8
  region, 36, 169
Finney, D. J., 95, 125, 133, 182
Fisher, Hans, 163, 173
Fisher, R. A., 4, 8, 29, 47
Functional relations, 3

Grouping, 16
  method of, 203

Haavelmo, T., 196
Hader, R. J., 207
Hansen, R. G., 163, 173

Hartley, H. O., 60
Hasel, A. A., 107
Hoel, P. G., 72, 81, 82, 83
Hotelling, H., 61, 72, 73, 74, 77, 78, 79, 80, 110, 165, 166
Hunter, J. S., 162
Hyperbola, fiducial boundary, 95, 102
  tolerance boundary, 99
Hyperbolic regression, 64
Hypothesis, 4

Independent variable, 11
  addition of, 34
  error in, 44, 161, 195, 196, 197, 203
  omission of, 34, 35
Index number, 197, 202
Information, 69
  combining of, 158
  matrix, 69
Instrumental variable, 204
Intercept, 10, 14, 44
Interpretation, of fiducial statements, 91
  of results, 3
Inverse estimation, 91, 95, 166
  fiducial limits, 96, 169
  tolerance limits, 99
Investigational variable, 204
Iterative methods, 19, 60

Jones, W. C., 107

Keeping, E. S., 61
Kloot, N. H., 72, 81, 82, 83
Kullback, S., 151

Lagrangian multiplier, 50
Lawrence, A. J., 39
Least squares, method of, 12, 166
Likelihood, 68
  maximum, method of, 68, 70
Lindley, D. V., 195, 197, 198
Linear compound variable, adequacy of, 74, 175, 184
Littler, G. F., 107

Mackney, A. W., 102
Matrix, auxiliary, 27, 28, 33
  final, 28
  inverse, 25, 29
  inversion of, 29

Matrix, of coefficients, 166
Maximum likelihood, method of, 68, 70
Maximum or minimum, 93
  of fitted curve, 110, 114
Multiple measurements, 175, 182
Multivariate analysis, 3, 176

Neyman, J., 93, 198, 204
Nonlinear function of parameters, 59
  estimation from, 105
Normal equations, 24, 170
Norton, H. W., 163, 173
Notation, 24, 130, 138, 152, 164
Null variate, 198, 205, 207

Omission of independent variable, 34, 35
One-tailed test, 76
Origin, regression through, 14, 42, 77
Over-all regression coefficient, 156
  test of hypothetical discriminator, 188

Parabola, maximum or minimum of, 110
Parallelism, test of, 131
Parameters, nonlinear function of, 59
  relations among, 195
  transformation of, 62
Partial regression coefficient, 29
Pimentel-Gomes, F., 62
Polynomial regression, 40
  significance tests on, 41
Polynomials, orthogonal, 45
Prior considerations, 5
Probability, direct, 91
  fiducial, 91
Proportional regressions, 149
Proportionality, constant of, 150, 204
  departure from, 150

Rao, C. R., 68, 183, 187, 188, 189, 190
Ratio, determinantal, 189
  estimation of, 92
  test of constancy of, 151
Reduced, sum of squares, 123
  variance, effective, 125
Reiersøl, O., 197, 204
Restricted coefficients, 50

Restrictions, linear, 49
  significance of, 55
Rosenblatt, H. M., 151
Roy, S. N., 3

Sandomire, M. M., 176
Scale convention, 177, 179
Scheffé, H., 8, 9
Schrumpf, W. M., 207
Schumacher, F. X., 107
Scott, E. L., 198, 204
Significance tests, 3
Simultaneous fiducial limits, 36, 169, 184
Smith, H. F., 202
Snedecor, G. W., 41
Stevens, W. L., 62
Sufficient statistics, 12, 60
Sulzberger, P. H., 119

Theoretical formulas, comparison of, 81, 83
Tocher, K. D., 138
Tolerance limits, 98
  inverse, 99
Transformation, of parameters, 62
  of variables, 18, 53
Trend, equation independent of, 57
Trial value, 62, 70

Variances and covariances, of coefficients, 25
  in simultaneous equations, 164
  restricted, 52, 86
  of inverse estimates, 168
  of regression functions, 95, 101, 164

Waerden, B. L. van der, 167
Wald, A., 203
Watson, R. H., 133
Weighting, 19, 156, 176
  adjustment of, 202
  with estimated weights, 67
Wilks, S. S., 83, 84, 85, 190
Williams, E. J., 72, 81, 82, 83, 123, 138, 192

Yates, F., 5, 47, 151, 152, 197, 202

Zero error, 15, 44
Zeros of fitted curve, 108